YORK NOTES

D0530654

TRANSLATIONS

BRIAN FRIEL

NOTES BY JOHN BRANNIGAN

Amended and updated by
TONY CORBETT

 Longman

York Press

YORK PRESS
322 Old Brompton Road, London SW5 9JH

PEARSON EDUCATION LIMITED
Edinburgh Gate, Harlow,
Essex CM20 2JE, United Kingdom
Associated companies, branches and representatives throughout the world

First published 2000
This new and fully revised edition first published 2004

10 9 8 7 6 5 4 3 2 1

ISBN 0–582–78438–7

Designed by Michelle Cannatella
Typeset by Land & Unwin (Data Sciences), Bugbrooke, Northamptonshire
Produced by Pearson Education North Asia Limited, Hong Kong

CONTENTS

PART ONE
INTRODUCTION

PART TWO
THE TEXT

PART THREE
CRITICAL APPROACHES

PART FOUR
CRITICAL HISTORY

PART FIVE
BACKGROUND

INTRODUCTION

HOW TO STUDY A PLAY

Studying on your own requires self-discipline and a carefully thought-out work plan in order to be effective.

- Drama is a special kind of writing (the technical term is 'genre') because it needs a performance in the theatre to arrive at a full interpretation of its meaning. Try to imagine that you are a member of the audience when reading the play. Think about how it could be presented on the stage, not just about the words on the page.

- Drama is always about conflict of some sort (which may be below the surface). Identify the conflicts in the play and you will be close to identifying the large ideas or themes which bind all the parts together.

- Make careful notes on themes, character, plot and any sub-plots of the play.

- Why do you like or dislike the characters in the play? How do your feelings towards them develop and change?

- Playwrights find non-realistic ways of allowing an audience to see into the minds and motives of their characters, for example, an aside or music. Consider how such dramatic devices are used in the play you are studying.

- Think of the playwright writing the play. Why were these particular arrangements of events, characters and speeches chosen?

- Cite exact sources for all quotations, whether from the text itself or from critical commentaries. Wherever possible find your own examples from the play to back up your opinions.

- Where appropriate, comment in detail on the language of the passage you have quoted.

- Always express your ideas in your own words.

These York Notes offer an introduction to *Translations* and cannot substitute for close reading of the text and the study of secondary sources.

CONTEXT

'Genre' is a type or category of literature, defined by common features or purpose. Drama, for example, is a distinct genre, because it requires staging. Within drama are many sub-genres such as 'kitchen-sink drama' (British realistic drama of the 1950s onwards) or 'Anglo-Irish Drama' (Irish drama written in English).

CONTEXT

Terms such as soliloquy etc. are known as 'theatrical conventions', or in Friel's own phrase: 'theatrical conceits'.

READING *TRANSLATIONS*

CONTEXT

The Ordnance Survey of Ireland aimed to produce the first standardised six-inches-to-the-mile map of the island of Ireland. In the process, the survey anglicised or standardised many Irish place names, thereby cutting many of them off from their etymology.

From its first performance in the Guild Hall, (London)Derry in 1980, *Translations* has entertained, informed and disturbed audiences around the world. It has been performed regularly in Ireland, England and the United States, and was, from the outset, proclaimed a modern classic by critics. It is indeed a play with an unusual power to show the best and the worst of human relationships and feelings, to combine comedy and tragedy to their fullest potential, but it is about much more than this. *Translations* ostensibly examines the impact of the Ordnance Survey of Ireland on a small corner of Donegal, in the extreme northwest of Ireland.

It purports to examine the effect of linguistic, cultural and political change on the lives and feelings of a handful of individuals in a small Irish village in 1833. Friel's play is partly concerned with the effect of historical changes on individuals and communities, and the play raises important questions about the nature of history, community, language and identity. Hugh, the school master, tells us that 'It is not the literal past, the "facts" of history, that shape us, but images of the past embodied in language ... we must never cease renewing those images' (p. 88). *Translations* could be seen as a play that does exactly what Hugh describes. It takes images from Irish history – of peasants with a love of learning, of English soldiers trampling the crops under their feet, of the people trying to eke out a living for themselves – and it interrogates (critically questions) those images. In doing so, it tells a story of love, war, misunderstanding, loyalty and betrayal. It can be read as a complex lesson specifically on Irish history, or it can be read as a tale of any two communities which are bitterly divided.

Translations is, to a far greater extent, a play about the source and nature of communication between cultures and between individuals. It examines how language shapes reality, and questions the assumption that any two people can share the same reality, or that ideas can be translated between cultures without being altered and transformed. In this way it is not a simple play about a turning-point in Irish history, although this is the springboard for Friel's meditation on the way in which cultures interact. Even the cliché images of Irish history are subject to scrutiny by the play. *Translations* can be interpreted in many different ways, but this is what makes it a rich and rewarding work of drama.

Translations was first produced in 1980 in Derry city in Northern Ireland. It was an instant success, and its first run was sold out. It received many excellent reviews and has remained a popular play ever since. This seems to be at odds with its rather obscure subject matter. The play is set in a hedge-school in a Gaelic-speaking area of northwestern Ireland in 1833 – not the most obvious recipe for theatrical success.

The events depicted in the play – involving an ordnance survey project and the introduction of a national system of elementary education – were unknown except to small academic circles. Reviewers seemed to be particularly impressed by two devices in the play, however. The first was the means by which Friel's play had the audience believe that they were hearing both Gaelic and English languages spoken when the play was presented entirely in English. The second was the powerful scene in Act II in which Yolland and Maire, an English soldier and an Irish peasant girl, find a way of conveying their love for each other without having a common language.

The dramatic devices of the play were innovative and original certainly, but the play had, and still has, a popular appeal which went beyond the admiration of theatre critics. *Translations*, to some observers, seemed to summarise, through events of local significance, the story of how one nation lost its language, culture and literature as a result of being conquered by another. It articulated the tragedy of Irish history over the course of several hundred years by telling a story about several days in the life of a fictitious Irish village in 1833. For those who were not versed in Irish history, the play offered a parable about the fate of an insular, antiquated people when they were exposed to an adventurous and modern empire. Because the people were insular and antiquated, they could not be translated into the modern world, and so were lost in the mists of time. This is why the play ends with Hugh

> **CONTEXT**
>
> 'Translation' has many different meanings, only some of which have to do with language. The *OED*'s primary meaning is: 'The removal or conveyance from one person, place, time, or condition to another'. It also includes: 'movement of a body or form of energy from one point of space to another', and only then comes to: 'the action or process of expressing the sense of a word, passage, etc., in a different language'. The dictionary also includes as sub-meanings, transformation, alteration, change, adaptation and the transfer of property.

CONTEXT

Under the penal laws in the seventeenth century, Catholic or Gaelic-language education was outlawed in Ireland. In defiance, Irish people set up secret 'hedge-schools', initially in hedgerows with a look-out nearby to warn of English officials or soldiers. When the laws were relaxed, the schools moved to barns or cow-sheds, like the one in this play. They were, in them-selves, symbols of resistance to British rule (see **Historical Background**).

struggling to remember what had happened to another lost civilisation, the Carthaginians. For *An Phoblacht*, the IRA newspaper, the play offered the hope that 'a man who does not know his seven times table [Doalty] can still have a deep instinct which is true and accurate' (Delaney 2000, p. 147). For others still, *Translations* is a parable of the way in which the Irish language and Gaelic culture became obsolete, even before the Survey of 1833.

While the play was immensely popular, it was also deeply controversial, not least because it was found to contain some serious distortions of historical facts. Reviewers and commentators pointed to exaggerations of the violence attributed to the soldiers who undertook the ordnance survey, errors in the depiction of the survey as a military campaign, and misrepresentations of the process of changing place names. It was criticised as a biased, inaccurate account of the events it purported to represent, and J. H. Andrews, on whose book *A Paper Landscape* Friel had based some of the play, despaired that it would be accepted by audiences as the truth when there were so many errors in it. Andrews went so far as to write an article entitled: 'Notes for a Future Edition of Brian Friel's Translations', which suggested that the play should be re-written to reflect the facts of the survey.

Friel was aware of having shaped and altered the historical facts for the purposes of dramatic fiction. That the soldiers of the ordnance survey did not carry bayonets and did not order evictions are among the many details that Friel changed or omitted. The accuracy of events in the play is not as important as what is represented by those events. Friel wanted to show that the renaming of Irish villages and townlands had as destructive an effect on Irish culture and society as a military invasion on Irish people. More importantly, he wanted to show how changing the names of the places in the landscape altered the landscape itself, by cutting it off from its etymological and morphological past.

The play was first produced at a time when the conflict in Northern Ireland between the British army and paramilitary organisations was particularly intense. Some critics believed that the play was simply exploiting the past to offer an anti-British interpretation of the present conflict. But the play is more complex in its representation of history and politics than this. The characters and incidents in the play do bear some relation to the conflict in Northern Ireland in the 1970s, but *Translations* has a great deal to say about language, translation, cultural differences and similarities, about the consequences of local, seemingly minor events in history and about the impact of historical and national changes on individuals, and these aspects of the play do not correspond exactly with such a reading.

Friel seems to be interested, not in giving us a one-sided story of events, but in the dilemmas and choices which have the potential to affect the course of history. In many of Friel's plays, at a precise moment in time, individuals face a dilemma which must be resolved, and which will have a decisive effect. In *Translations*, to take one example, Owen and Yolland face the dilemma of what to call a place called 'Tobair Vree', which is named after a man who fell down a well there. Owen asks: 'Do we scrap Tobair Vree altogether and call it – what? – The Cross? Crossroads? Or do we keep piety with a man long dead, long forgotten, his name "eroded" beyond recognition, whose trivial little story nobody in the parish remembers?' (Act II scene 1, p. 44). Friel indicates that the answer to the question will affect the future of Irish language, culture and history, even if only in a small, local way.

The achievement of Brian Friel in *Translations* is that he brings us to the realisation that every little, personal, local story – of love, hope, loss and change – is connected intimately and subtly to the course of history. As to what each story means, and how each character should have dealt with her or his dilemma, he leaves that to the audience or reader to decide.

CONTEXT

As an example of changing names, *Dún na nGall*, which meant 'the foreigners' stronghold' became the pleasant-sounding but meaningless *Donegal*.

PART TWO

THE TEXT

A NOTE ON THE TEXT

Brian Friel's Translations *was published first by Faber & Faber in 1981, following the first performance of the play in the Guildhall in Derry on 23 September 1980 by the Field Day Theatre Company. This remains the standard edition, and is the edition used in these Notes.* Translations *is also available in* Brian Friel: Plays 1, *Faber & Faber, 1996, with an introduction by Seamus Deane; and in an anthology of Irish drama and criticism, which includes notes and critical writings on the play: John P. Harrington, ed.,* Modern Irish Drama, *Norton & Company, 1991.*

SYNOPSIS

The plot of the play is very simple: to the village of Baile Beag, Donegal, Ireland, in 1833, come the British Army, conducting the first accurate cartological survey of the island of Ireland. As a part of this survey, the team are required to anglicise and standardise place names.

The village of Baile Beag, and, by extension, the island as a whole, are represented in microcosm by the pupils and teachers in the hedge-school. The long opening Act sets the scene for the rest of the play, and introduces the main themes. The tone at the beginning is light, with plenty of comic moments, but there is a darker undertone, represented by the physical afflictions of Manus and Sarah, and the approach of the soldiers. Captain Lancey of the Royal Engineers is represented as a cliché 'little Englander', full of his own importance, but knowing little. As the play progresses, he will show a more ruthless side. Yolland, a young lieutenant, besotted with the Irish countryside and people, counterpoints Lancey's blatant colonial attitude. Owen, Hugh's younger and more successful son, is employed by the survey as a translator. Although Yolland considers him a friend, he mishears his name as 'Roland' (Act I, p. 32). In Act II scene 1, Owen and Yolland are engaged in the business of translation, arguing over the process by which the culture of one

CONTEXT

'*Baile Beag*' means a small town in Gaelic, suggesting the town could be anywhere. Friel is also emphasising the small, limited scope of such a community, its insularity and its lack of opportunity. Friel set several of his plays in Baile Beag, or its anglicised equivalent, Ballybeg. In *Philadelphia, Here I Come*, it is a stagnant, rural backwater, full of people lost in their own delusions because their small lives.

language is to be transferred into another, and considering the amount that will be lost. Yolland is, in ways, more sympathetic than Owen, but this stems from a naïve view of Ireland as a prelapsarian world.

Hugh joins them, making slighting comparisons between English and Latin, but it is Hugh who recognises that the Gaelic language 'no longer matches the landscape of...fact' (Act II scene 1, p.52) His mood is elegiac, as if he expects the end to come, even if he does not know the manner of it. After Hugh leaves, Manus enters. He has had a meeting with some men from Inish Meadhon, an island off the coast. They want him to start a hedge-school there. He is anxious to tell Maire, as this post would give him the means to marry. Maire, however, is more interested in Yolland. In the famous second scene of Act II, Yolland and Maire have slipped away from a dance, and are running hand-in-hand. A peculiar love-scene ensues, where, although neither can understand the other's language, meaning between them becomes plain. The scene ends with a kiss, witnessed by Sarah, who rushes to tell Manus. In Act III, Manus is preparing to leave, alone. Yolland, it becomes apparent, went missing the night of the dance. Owen is of the opinion that if Manus leaves now, suspicion will fall on him. Already reinforcements have arrived and the soldiers are searching. Lancey orders livestock shot, and large-scale evictions of the populace if Yolland is not found. We are given the impression that the Donnelly twins have captured, or murdered Yolland. The play ends with Hugh agreeing to teach English to Maire, something he has always resisted. With this knowledge, she can emigrate. In a closing speech, Hugh remembers the founding (and, presumably, the fated destruction) of Carthage.

While a synopsis of the plot is a useful tool, it really tells us very little about the play. *Translations* is about the relationships between people who speak different languages and come from different cultures.

It presents a stark opposition between the Irish people of Baile Beag who speak Gaelic and who trace their roots to ancient civilisation and the English soldiers who speak English and who seem to be unaware of much outside their own culture. Manus, Doalty and Bridget are suspicious of the soldiers, and suspect that the map the soldiers are making is not so harmless as Owen wants them to

CONTEXT

'Prelapsarian', meaning before the Fall, is a synonym for rural perfection. Many commentators see the Gaelic world of *Translations* as pure and unspoilt, ravished by the invading British. Friel's relationship with the Irish landscape, however, is ambiguous. In *The Communication Cord*, he lampoons the idea of the Gaelic idyll. In *Wonderful Tennessee* he subjects it to a postChristian **deconstruction**.

believe. On the other hand, Hugh and Maire seem to tolerate, and even like, the presence of the soldiers. There are differences in how the English soldiers react to the Irish characters too. Lancey treats the people of Baile Beag with indifference at first, and brutally towards the end of the play. Yolland, however, falls in love with the people and the place, describing it as 'really heavenly' (Act II scene 1, p. 45) But even for the characters who are enthusiastic to communicate with each other, as is the case with Yolland and Maire, there are problems with language and translation between the two cultures which have tragic consequences in store.

It is the tension between these characters from different cultures and with very different personalities which propels the action of the play forward. Friel's play examines the impact of political conflicts on human relationships in one small community in a few days. For Yolland, Maire, Owen, Manus, Lancey and Hugh, the events of those few days test their allegiances and aspirations.

Act I establishes the identities of the characters, and situates them in relation to each other. In Act II, some of the characters are shown responding to changes in their circumstances. Owen and Yolland must gauge their own feelings about the changes which they are participating in imposing on Baile Beag and the surrounding areas. Maire and Yolland struggle to find a way of communicating their feelings to each other despite language and cultural barriers. In the final Act, circumstances change beyond the control of the characters. Lancey is forced to respond to the disappearance of Yolland. The inhabitants of Baile Beag must examine their own feelings about the brutal response of the English soldiers and their part in precipitating that response.

Although there are comic and entertaining scenes in the play, in the concluding Act it becomes more sombre and tragic. It is presumed that the Donnelly twins have harmed Yolland in some way 'as a gesture'. But gestures usually invite replies, and Lancey replies with the language of violence and threat. The undercurrents of distrust and misunderstanding which pervade between the characters in the rest of the play come out in the open in the final Act, in which we see the lasting damage of divided political and cultural loyalties.

CONTEXT

For the people of Baile Beag, compromise is no longer possible. Circumstances have polarised the Irish and the English, and the violent on both sides assume command. Moderation, in the person of Manus, abandons the place, and wisdom, represented by Hugh, forgets.

The people of Baile Beag feel that they are dispossessed of their ancient traditions and ways of life, and that they are poised on the brink of disaster. Hugh's loss of memory, and his talk of a community which could have been idyllic but which was instead destroyed, illustrate this **tragedy** as the play draws to a close.

DETAILED SUMMARIES

ACT I

- In a hedge-school in the townland of Baile Beag, Manus, the son of Hugh, the drunken school-teacher, and in love with Maire, is giving a lesson.
- We learn that an ordinance survey is to be carried out by English soldiers, headed by Lancey.
- Owen, Hugh's other son, arrives from the city and we learn that he is friendly with one of the English officers.

The play opens in the hedge-school, a disused hay barn. As they wait for Hugh, the drunken schoolmaster, his son, Manus, who is lame, tries to teach Sarah, who is mute, to speak her name.

Manus uses speech exercises to help her to relax and articulate. They are watched by Jimmy Jack Cassie who is reading Homer's *Odyssey* in Greek. Jimmy, an elderly bachelor with a penchant for reading Greek and Latin **classics** and a mild obsession with sex, is known, with affectionate **irony**, as 'the Infant Prodigy' (p. 3). He recites with evident enjoyment, occasionally relying on Manus for a translation. Sarah who evidently has feelings for Manus, and gives him some flowers she has picked. As he kisses her in thanks, Maire enters, to Manus's great embarrassment. He is in love with Maire, and hopes to marry her. The conversation between Maire and Jimmy makes it clear that they are speaking in Irish, not English, but it also indicates that all is not well between them. Maire is impatient of the fact that Manus has no income, and will not apply for the job as headmaster in the new National School because Hugh, his father, expects it to come to him.

CONTEXT

In response to the growing demand for education, a state system of education, which became known as National Schools, was established. They were provided free of charge at elementary or primary level. The English language was the sole medium of instruction in the new National Schools, and they were therefore partly responsible for the decline of the Irish language.

CONTEXT

The 'sweet smell' (p. 17) refers to rotting potatoes. In the early nineteenth century, the Irish came to depend on the potato. Crops failed many times during the nineteenth century, including the year in which the play is set. Between 1845 and 1850 crops failed completely, causing the death of over a million people, and forcing over a million more to emigrate. This catastrophe, known as the Great Famine, had a devastating impact on the Irish people.

CONTEXT

Doalty is inventing 'St Colmcille's' prophecy (p. 18) that there would never be potato blight in Baile Beag. This famous Donegal saint was a sixth-century monk who founded monasteries in Doire (now [London]Derry), and on Iona.

The entry of Doalty and Bridget changes the direction of the scene, and introduces the theme of the ordnance survey. Doalty has stolen the surveyor's pole, and is in high spirits, indulging in impressions of Hugh's pompous and overblown mode of speech.

As they prepare for the lesson the talk turns to the potato crop. There is a worry every year that blight will destroy the crop, leading to famine. Manus discovers Maire looking at a map of the United States, and she reveals that she is now in a position to emigrate, if she wishes.

When Hugh turns up, he is slightly drunk, and he begins to tell the class news of the soldiers and their work in making an ordnance survey of the area. He explains that he has invited the officer in charge of the ordnance survey to talk to the pupils about the purposes of the survey. He is interrupted by Maire, who complains that she wants to learn English, a language which will be much more useful if she is to emigrate to England or America than the Greek and Latin which Hugh is teaching them.

As there is 'no man in the house' (p. 16) Maire's options are limited. She faces the prospect either of marrying someone with a stable job or emigrating to find work so that she can send money back to her family. For this she needs English. Hugh ignores her, and proceeds to tell them about the opening of the new National School nearby, of which, he says, Mr George Alexander, Justice of the Peace, has promised him the headship.

Hugh is then interrupted by the arrival of his son, Owen, '*dressed smartly – a city man*' (p. 26). He is a merchant in Dublin and has been hired as a translator with the English soldiers who are engaged in the ordnance survey. He says his job is to: 'translate the quaint, archaic tongue you people persist in speaking into the King's good English' (p. 30). Owen is echoing the view of a stereotypical English colonist, here, which may be read as meaning that either he has become loyal to English colonial interests in Ireland, or that he is trying to rile the others, or both.

As a merchant in Dublin, Owen leads a very different lifestyle to that of his family in Baile Beag. He belongs to an anglicised middle class of merchants who benefitted from the expansion of Dublin's commercial ventures, and this is what has evidently brought him into contact with British army officers. When he refers to the people of Baile Beag, he uses the word '*civilised*' (p. 29) **ironically**, indicating that he regards them as uncivilised, or that he is trying to provoke a reaction from them. He may also be echoing the received opinion of the British soldiers. When he announces that 'I'm on their pay-roll' (p. 30), the is informing the others that he has gone into the service of the British army. To the Donnelly twins, and possibly also to Doalty, this would be regarded as treason.

Owen introduces two English officers, Captain Lancey and Lieutenant Yolland, to the others, and translates Lancey's announcements about the purpose of the survey. But Owen does not translate exactly what Lancey is saying. He keeps the translation short, and abbreviates Lancey's statements throughout, altering the meaning of these statements by removing anything he feels would be interpreted as controversial by local people. Owen's hesitation before using the word 'correct' (p. 35) suggests that he knows there is something sinister about translating the names, or that he knows the people will be suspicious of it.

Clearly, the use of the map for reassessing taxation and for military intelligence would not be greeted favourably. Manus reprimands him afterwards for neglecting to translate Lancey's statement that the survey would serve military as well as civil purposes. Yolland, meanwhile, is shy and reserved, and says very little. His task, specifically, is to standardise and anglicise the names on the map.

The final dialogue of the Act is between Owen and Manus. Manus reprimands Owen for mistranslating Lancey's speech. Owen shows himself to be slippery here, relying on a defence of ambiguity in poetry to justify his deliberate falsification of Lancey's words. To Manus, there is no 'ambiguity' (p. 36) or difficulty with the place names, and he knows that the agenda of Lancey's operation is to remove the Gaelic names and replace them with English ones.

Owen has taken on the responsibility not just of interpreting, but of acting as go-between between the two cultures – British and Irish.

> **CONTEXT**
>
> The name of 'Mr George Alexander' (p. 25) suggests a man of English descent. This was typical for men in positions of power in Ireland in colonial times, particularly in positions of trust, such as Justice of the Peace.

CONTEXT

The technique of 'triangulation' (p. 33) meant dividing areas into right-angled triangles. By measuring the base and three angles, the other sides are calculated trigonometrically without having to be measured, so minimising the amount of work involved.

This is, indeed, what he signifies in the play, someone who is able to straddle both cultures, but who is perhaps out of sorts in both cultures too.

Between them they represent two of the attitudes to the British in the play. Owen, successful in his own right, does not see them as a threat. He sees no problem in the changes about to be made to the place names, and accepts 'Roland' (p. 36) as an equivalent of his own name. George is obviously friendly with Owen, but the fact that he gets his name wrong implies that there are serious, unresolved differences between them yet. As an innacurate 'translation' (p. 36) it also has a bearing on the main theme of the play. Owen reveals his careless attitude to his own name ('It's only a name', p. 37) and to the place names he will soon be translating. His argument – 'It's the same me' (p. 37) – assumes that an object is the same, regardless of its name. This contrasts with his view later, when he tells his father that he will not be able to find his way around the local areas now that the place names have been changed.

Manus, on the other hand, is uneasy, seeing the military operation as a threat, and the removal or replacement of the familiar place names as unnecessary and sinister. The third attitude, outright violence, is never shown on stage, but is alluded to in the references to the Donnelly twins.

COMMENTARY

This simple lesson at the beginning of the play introduces the main theme: the problems of communication, language and translation which have been the root causes of violence and conflict. Communication is difficult, and is always an act of translation – from thought to words, from one language to another, from one culture to another. When Sarah succeeds in speaking her name, she is making the first act of translation in the play, translating silence into speech. In the final Act, however, Sarah returns to silence, and this is just one example of the failures of communication which resound through the play.

A number of phrases in the Act remind us that the characters are not speaking English: 'Fit me better if I had even that much English'

(p. 8) the first sign to the audience that the characters are supposed to be speaking in the Irish language; 'Sure you know I have only Irish like yourself' (p. 8) at this point the play confirms to the audience that the characters are supposed to be speaking in the Irish language; and 'bo-som' (p. 9) which Jimmy pronounces awkwardly, indicating that it is not in his native language. It suggests, like his earlier ruminations on Homer's goddesses, that he is obsessed with sexual matters.

The first act of *Translations* defines clearly the characters and relationships which will be the focus of the rest of the play. In drama, characters are usually first experienced by sight, that is, when they first appear on stage. There are notable exceptions in this play. Hugh and the English soldiers are mentioned before they are seen. This alerts the audience to the importance of these characters, who are obviously of great interest to the others. But for those characters who are not mentioned, their first appearance on stage establishes in the audience's minds something of their personality, and how they fit into the story. The physical appearance and *'shabby'* dress of Manus (p. 1), for example, distinguishes him from his brother, Owen, who is dressed *'smartly'* (p. 26). Owen is described as *'a city man'* (p. 26) and is dressed to appear different to the other natives of Baile Beag, as he has become a businessman in Dublin. His modern, smart dress will distinguish him from the peasant appearance of his father's pupils.

Hugh enters *'shabbily dressed, carrying a stick'* (p. 20). Each of these visual details tells us a lot about the characteristics of each person. Manus's shabby appearance tells us that he is poor and down-to-earth. Owen, on the other hand, has pulled himself out of poverty to a more comfortable lifestyle, and is more prosperous and at ease than Manus. Hugh is dressed shabbily like Manus, but his stick, always the schoolmaster's weapon, conveys his air of dignity and, of course, his pomposity.

It is in details such as these that the differences and tensions between the characters are revealed. Lancey's appearance, for example, is described as *'crisp'* (p. 31). This contrasts with Hugh's slight drunkenness and slovenliness. These are, on one level, differences merely in personality. But they are also emblematic of

> **? QUESTION**
>
> How far does Friel succeed in making his themes universal? Is the play primarily about the ancient and on-going enmity between the islands of Britain and Ireland, or does it have relevance to other cultural clashes, contemporary and historical?

CHECK THE BOOK

Language and the limits of language are themes to which Friel returns again and again. In his play that followed *Translations, The Communication Cord,* 1983, Friel undercuts and lampoons many of the sentiments found in the earlier play. Many languages are thrown into this farce, and misunderstandings are rife. In *Dancing at Lughnasa,* 1990, Friel moves beyond words into music and dance to convey feelings and sentiments that he considers inexpressible in mere words.

wider cultural and social differences between them, which account partly for the conflict between the Irish and English characters. Lancey is proud of his '*crisp*' manner, and, in his eyes, it marks him out as superior to the '*foreign civilians*' (p. 31). Yet when Jimmy asks him in Latin if he knows the language, 'Nonne Latine loquitur?' (p. 32), Lancey reveals his ignorance by saying that he does not speak Gaelic, thinking that it is in that language that Jimmy has addressed him.

Hugh values words and learning, which is evident in his enthusiasm for knowledge and literature, and does not value appearances or material wealth, which is obvious from his own style of dress. Hugh and Lancey hold two very different sets of values and beliefs, then, and the differences between them are reflected in the actions and events of the rest of the play.

GLOSSARY

1	*byre* cow-shed
1	*battle of hay* a small bale of hay
2	*Homer* reputedly the author of the Greek epics, *The Iliad* and *The Odyssey*, thought to have lived sometime between the ninth and seventh centuries BC
4	*Athene* daughter of Zeus, goddess of wisdom, and of the city of Athens. Jimmy is reading from Book XIII of *The Odyssey*, where Athene appears to Ulysses to tell him that she will guide him through his ordeals and lead him home
4	*Ulysses* hero of *The Odyssey*. Renowned as a cunning and courageous schemer
5	*Diarmuid's Grania* (from Irish mythology) To avoid marrying the elderly Fionn Mac Cumhaill, Grainne used magic to send everyone at the feast before the wedding asleep, except for Diarmuid. She demanded that he rescue her from the marriage. Fionn, angry on discovering that the two had fled, began his pursuit of them. Grania represents passion, ruthlessness and independence.
5	*Artemis* daughter of Zeus and goddess of the young, renowned as a huntress, armed with bow and quiver, and patroness of young women athletes

5	**Helen of Troy** daughter of Zeus, the most beautiful woman in the world. She was abducted by Paris who carried her off to Troy. The Greek leaders, including Ulysses, organised the campaign to win her back, and so began the Trojan War.
5	**Zeus** the most powerful god in Greek mythology. He is known for his power, ruling over the fate of humankind, and wielding weapons of thunder and lightning. But he is also known for his love affairs, and his many offspring
8	*Esne fatigata?* Are you tired? Jimmy has switched to speaking Latin
9	**Diana** Roman name for Greek goddess, Artemis
9	**Nova Scotia** province on east coast of Canada, one of the closest parts of North America to Ireland
10	**Sapper** a soldier of the Royal Engineers
10	**surveyor's pole** a striped pole which land surveyors use to take measurements and angles
11	**Red Coats** (colloquial) soldiers of the British army who traditionally wore red uniforms
11	**a great aul shaft for your churn** Doalty is suggesting on one level that the surveyor's pole could be useful to Bridget to stir the butter in her churn, but he is also making a crude sexual innuendo here, hence Bridget's reaction
13	**bucks** (slang) men, as male deer, rabbit or hare
13	**Satires of Horace** Quintus Horatius Flaccus (65–8BC) was a Roman lyric poet and satirist, famous for his *Odes* and *Epistles*.
14	**Virgil's *Georgics*** Virgil (70–19BC) celebrated Roman poet, renowned for his poem on the founding of Rome, *The Aeneid*, and for his *Eclogues* and *Georgics*.
15	**the *Agricola* of Tacitus** Roman commander who ruled over Britain in the first century AD and who conquered parts of northern England and southern Scotland
19	**yella meal** yellow meal, finely ground and used for porridge. An equivalent term would be 'mincemeat'
20	**jouk** (colloquial) look
20	**I'm dying about you** I really like you, I'm mad about you

continued

CONTEXT

In the nineteenth century over 8 million people emigrated from Ireland, mostly to the USA, from where family members would send back money to pay for others to follow. This money was known as 'passage money' (p. 16).

21	**Pliny Minor** Gaius Plinius Caecilius Secundus (AD62–c.112), nephew of Pliny the Elder, and a Roman letter-writer. An administrator in the Roman empire, he is most renowned for his description of the eruption of Vesuvius
22	**Sophocles from Colonus** Greek playwright (496–406BC), famous for his Theban plays and the character of Oedipus. Hugh is mocking Dan Doalty's abilities as a student by comparing him with Sophocles, but quoting Sophocles telling us that ignorance is bliss
25	**Euripides** Greek dramatist (480–406BC), and contemporary of Sophocles; renowned for his tragedies
26	**Hugh Mor O'Donnell** Owen is addressing his father as Hugh O'Donnell the great. 'Mór' means big or great and signifies seniority and prestige in Gaelic families
27	**Poteen** home-brewed alcoholic drink, made from potatoes, or from fermented grain
28	**Omagh** town in county Tyrone, southeast of where the play is set
31	**neither a roof … nor a sod of ground** Maire is chastising Manus for talking of marriage when he has no house of his own and no land on which to grow food
32	**aqua vitae** water of life, which in Gaelic – uisce beatha – refers to whisky
34	**'Ireland … the interests of Ireland'** Lancey is quoting from a statement made by the Spring Rice committee on 21 June 1824 recommending that ordnance survey work begin in Ireland and claiming that the mapping of the entire country was proof that the British government had Ireland's interests in mind

ACT II SCENE 1

- Yolland and Hugh argue over place names.
- Manus announces that he has been offered a job.
- Hugh discourses on Irish culture.
- Maire is attracted to Yolland.

Yolland and Hugh are involved principally in filling in the place names on to the new maps of the area, their work lubricated by liberal amounts of poteen. It becomes clear that their work is controversial, because it involves anglicising the Gaelic names. This is done in two main ways – either by finding an equivalent English translation (Bun na hAbhann, literally 'the end of the river' becomes the more elegant 'Burnfoot' p. 40), or by anglicising the name until it sounds English (Baile Beag becomes not 'Smalltown', but the meaningless 'Ballybeg' p. 45). The work is slow, partly because they are drinking and partly because Yolland begins to have serious problems with anglicising names which he has come to love. He and Owen begin to argue about some of the changes to the names. Manus then enters, busying himself with menial tasks. His hostility to Yolland is emphasised by the fact that he refuses to speak English.

Manus is suspicious of Yolland who is very friendly with the Irish, whereas Lancey is a familiar figure of English colonial authority. Yolland puzzles Manus because it is less clear whose 'side' Yolland is on, the side whose uniform he is wearing, or the side of those with whom he seems to be building up a rapport.

Friel complicates Yolland's character by having him ask about the Donnelly twins. It would be uninteresting to make Yolland a simple hibernophile. Yolland is asking Owen a question about suspected rebels, and so it is unclear what his motives are. He may be simply curious about who the twins are or he may be trying to win some intelligence information from Owen for his superior, Lancey.

Hugh's entrance adds to the discussion of the relevance of Irish culture to the modern world. Surprisingly, for all his denigration of the English, Hugh has a clear picture of the future of the Irish language, suspecting that it 'no longer matches the landscape of…fact' (p. 53). Manus re-enters and announces his news that he has been offered a teaching job on a nearby island. He tells Maire his news as soon as she enters, and seems to propose marriage to Maire, asking her how she would like to live with him on an island. But she hardly notices him, and seems to be distracted by Yolland.

> **CONTEXT**
>
> The place names in the scene translate as follows: Poll na gCaorach: the hole of the sheep, Baile Beag: small town, Ceann Balor: the head(land) of Balor (a mythical Irish god-king), Lis Maol: fort of the dense (or bald), Machaire Buidhe: yellow plain, Baile na nGall: town of the foreigners, Carraig an Ri: rock of the king, Mullach Dearg: red top or peak, Loch an Iubhair: lake of the yew, Bun na hAbhann: the end (mouth) of the river, Tra Bhan: white beach.

COMMENTARY

It is clear from the beginning of this scene that Yolland is less than enthusiastic about his role in anglicising place names. He relishes the Gaelic names, even if he pronounces them poorly. Later, he argues with Owen to preserve the original Gaelic names, and he is depicted falling in love with Baile Beag. For him it represents a different way of life to what he has been accustomed to in England.

Yolland is an idealist, who feels sentimental about Baile Beag and romanticises it as 'heavenly' (p. 45). He stands up for his principles – even when it comes to what seem to others trivial details, such as the name of Tobair Vree. Owen, on the other hand, is a pragmatist, who seems to be indifferent to the fate of the place names of his homeland, and careless even about whether his own name is pronounced correctly.

The differences between Yolland and Owen in this scene illuminate the debates about the anglicisation of place names as well as informing us of their character traits. The argument over the name of Tobair Vree, in particular, allows both sides of the case to be presented. Owen argues that the name derives from an event which everybody has forgotten, and so is therefore no longer relevant. Yolland clings to the name because it has a history, even if forgotten. It has sentimental value, if nothing else. Yolland recognises that the work that he is doing with Owen does have a sinister aspect, and this has probably come about after he witnessed Owen showing his father that without the familiar Gaelic names, the places around them don't have the same meaning or significance (p. 51).

There is more at stake here than a mere re-naming. The discussion shows that the Irish approach to landscape and place names is older, it is oral and more fluid. Names have attached to places over time – not always the same name for everyone, not always one name to one place. The British approach is written, standard and rigid, very much at odds with the Irish.

Owen defends what they are doing by telling Yolland that the Gaelic names are confusing, and that the new names will standardise

(p. 52) them. It is unclear to what extent Owen really believes that this is not a sinister exercise, and to what extent he is defending their jobs just for expediency.

The centre of the scene is the exchange between Yolland and Hugh. Yolland has just lamented the fact that one may understand a language, but be unable to speak 'the language of the tribe' (p. 48), by which he means the innumerable nuances of a language and of a dialect, formed over generations, and instinctive and unnoticed by native speakers. To an extent, Yolland is correct when he speaks of the core of a language as 'hermetic' (p. 48).

Hugh tells Yolland 'it can happen that a civilisation can be imprisoned in a linguistic contour which no longer matches the landscape of ... fact' (p. 43). Hugh is being pragmatic, he sees the fact that his way of life is at an end, but he is not pragmatic in the same way as Owen, who embraces the English way of life. Instead, Hugh will become extinct with his culture, which is why his speeches here have an elegiac tone. In a sense, it might appear that Manus is the idealist in that he refuses to compromise because of Yolland's presence, and continues to speak in Gaelic. We may, however, attribute his motives as much to jealousy over Maire's attachment to Yolland as to any sense of cultural loyalty. It is ironic, therefore, at the end of the play that Yolland has disappeared and Manus has run off, while the two pragmatists, Owen and Hugh, have adapted to the changing circumstances around them and have survived.

> **CONTEXT**
>
> 'Hermetic' means secret, sealed, unattainable. Friel draws here on modern philosophers of language, who see the constructs and meanings of language as constantly shifting. Friel has a particular interest in the idea of 'language games' as presented by the Austrian philosopher Ludwig Wittgenstein.

GLOSSARY

38	Creel a wicker basket
38	reference books church registries, lists of landowners and tenants, grand jury lists, etc. which Owen and Yolland are using to help them decide on place names for the map
39	Banowen ... Owenmore ... Binhone Owen and Yolland are finding that previous attempts to record the name of Bun na hAbhann in official documents have not been able to agree

continued

Act II scene 1 continued

CHECK THE BOOK

Friel explores the themes of people and history/politics in many of his plays. Two in particular that are worth reading in tandem with *Translations* are *The Freedom of the City*, in which the actual happenings are contrasted with official and media reports, and *Making History*, in which the 'historian' Lombard creates an heroic history, regardless of the actual facts.

39	**Freeholders** those who have tenure over land for a guaranteed period for a fee
39	**neither fish nor flesh** neither one thing nor the other
42	**your man** him, this man
43	**there are always the Rolands** 'the Rolands' in this case would mean the people who are willing to betray their own side and desert to help the enemy
44	**addled** confused
46	**capped** stopped or fenced in
47	**East India Company** a trading company founded in London in 1600 by royal charter to open up British trade in the Far East. The quintessential colonial organisation
47	**Waterloo** the battle of Waterloo, 18 June 1815, near Brussels in which Napoleon was finally defeated by a force of British, Dutch, Belgian, German and Prussian troops led by the Duke of Wellington
47	**Bastille** French revolutionaries stormed the prison of Bastille, symbol of state authority, on 14 July 1789. The date of the fall of the Bastille is celebrated in France as a national holiday
48	**Apollo** Greek and Roman god of intelligence, music, poetry and healing
48	**Cuchulainn** (Irish mythology) warrior hero, Cuchulainn is chiefly famous for his defence of Ulster against the armies of Queen Medb of Connacht, at which battle he was forced to slay his best friend, Ferdia.
48	**Paris** (Greek mythology) Paris was rewarded with the most beautiful woman in the world, Helen, for favouring Aphrodite in a disagreement among goddesses. Helen was in love with another suitor, however, and Paris stole her away to Troy, thus sparking off the Trojan war
49	**Ovid** Publius Ovidius Naso (43BC – AD18), Roman writer of *Metamorphoses*, a narrative of various stories of transformation, in which characters are often transformed into images of their desire
49	**plebeian** uncultured or coarse, although Hugh is probably referring to its use in ancient Rome, meaning of low birth or common
49	*expeditio* (Latin) expedition

49	**journeyman tailor** a qualified tailor who works for another tailor, thereby living in his shadow, or not able to show off his true talents. It can also mean that the tailor is simply hired from day to day, and has a precarious livelihood
49	**William Wordsworth** English Romantic poet (1770–1850), best known for his *Lyrical Ballads* with Samuel T. Coleridge, and *The Prelude*. One of the most famous English poets at the time in which this play is set, so it is incredible that Hugh has not heard of him
51	**Pentaglot Preceptor** teacher of five languages
52	**I understand … not immortal** Hugh advises Yolland that he should not feel isolated or alienated by a foreign language, such as Gaelic, for languages change and are pliable
53	**Tobair Vree** from Tobair Bhriain – the well of Brian. The 'bh' is pronounced 'v', and the 'n' became silent over a period of years
56	**speak in English … colonist?** Manus's response to Owen's request to speak in English shows growing contempt for Yolland and suspicion of his motives
57	**Inis Meadhon** middle island. A part of the Aran islands off the coast of County Clare.
57	**a rood of standing corn** a quarter of an acre of corn
57	**twelve drills of potatoes** twelve rows of potatoes
57	**£42 a year** a decent salary on which to get married and settle down
59	**How will you like living on an island?** This is Manus's way of asking Maire to marry him, or his way of assuming that she will

CONTEXT

Yolland's reference to Wordsworth (p. 41) is not an extraneous detail, but aligns him with the early Romantic movement. Wordsworth believed in the moral power of the countryside, and wrote many poems on the power of nature, of which *The Prelude* is the most developed, and *Tintern Abbey* one the most accessible.

ACT II SCENE 2

- Maire and Yolland are falling in love.
- Sarah witnesses them and runs off to tell Manus.

Maire and Yolland have fallen in love, and this is evident when they emerge from a dance together.

CONTEXT

The Oxford Companion to Literature writes of Friel: 'His great theme is the gulf between private experience and the public world'. This is certainly true of the relationship between Maire and Yolland, as in public life they are on opposite sides.

At first Maire is shy, and the two find it difficult to communicate as neither speaks the other's language. Yolland has no Irish, and Maire only one stumbling phrase and a few odd words of English, yet they manage to communicate their affection perfectly, their contrasting languages, although expressed entirely through English, merging and diverging like themes in a duet. They begin to communicate through the mechanics of the languages, rather than through their content. Yolland begins by carefully pronouncing the Gaelic place names which he has come to love. She responds, and together they recite a litany of names which becomes poetic. They caress and express their love for each other.

Sarah enters and discovers them kissing.

COMMENTARY

This short love-scene is a triumph of theatricality, and a major element in Friel's developing theory of communication.

The dramatic tension between Maire and Yolland has been building up on stage since Act I. When Yolland first appears in front of the people of Baile Beag, shy and quiet, Maire asks to hear him speak, the first sign that she is interested in him. In Act II scene 1, she asks Owen to tell Yolland of the dance. She also tells Owen that they have been waving to each other across the fields. In this scene, however, they are alone together for the first time, and both are clearly nervous.

In some ways, this is a simple romantic scene, but with an important difference. The lovers do not have a language in common, and so they must attempt to discover a way of communicating their feelings for each other. The solution, after disastrous attempts in Latin and English, is to whisper to each other the Gaelic place names which Yolland has been employed to change. In the recitation of Gaelic place names, the simple, effective: 'what what?' and 'sorry-sorry?' and the mutually used phrase 'O my God' (p. 63), draw them nearer together, but for the audience, not for the characters themselves. One might infer that Friel is using the similarities of the human thought process to indicate that understanding and closeness are possible without language, even though the speakers of language are unaware of these possibilities. They move from the constructions of language to the sounds of language: water, fire, earth, Druim Dubh, Poll na gCaorach, Lios Maol. Maire joins in Yolland's recitation of place names as they map out an imaginary topography which brings them physically closer together. They appear, by the end of the scene, to be aware of what the other is saying.

The poetic recitation of the names is the key which unlocks the intimacy between them. This is perhaps because to most audiences the names are in an unknown language and are therefore exotic. Reciting the names in English doesn't have quite the same effect – rivermouth, blackridge, sheepsrock, and so on. (But in the final Act, Maire will also recite some English place names which are equally poetic in effect.)

The writing is skilful, because it is just possible from the context that what they are saying is caused by the passionate repetition of 'always' (p. 52) and the fact that thay are both trembling.

Both Maire and Yolland are curious about the word for 'always' in each other's language. There is **irony** for both, of course, in their failure to recognise the word. 'Always' can mean very little in a community and language which is threatened with extinction, and in their relationship, which will turn out to be short-lived.

If that were the only purpose of the writing, then it would be merely appealing and clever, and could be admired or even dismissed as such. It works because both languages, at this point, are seen to understand the world in the same way. The rest of the play is taken up with the recital of the differences in perception between the Irish and English, with the impossibility of understanding the tribe. Here the decoding process becomes irrelevant. Maire and Yolland move beyond language, speaking only in sounds, without recourse to meanings. The language process becomes important again when Sarah enters and discovers them kissing. It is Manus who has taught her to speak, and now the words she speaks will precipitate the tragic ending of the play.

? QUESTION

In *Translations*, does Friel come down on one side or the other of the conflict, does he nudge the audience towards a particular viewpoint, or does he even-handedly set out the plot and allow room for differing views?

GLOSSARY

49   The grass ... is soaking Maire and Yolland are speaking in different languages, and they are also thinking in different ways. Maire deduces that the grass is wet because her feet are soaking, whereas Yolland deduces that her feet must be wet because the grass is soaking

51   in Norfolk ... first of May Maire's curious phrase which she has learned from her Aunt Mary, does mean something to Yolland, who begins to tell her about maypole dancing in his mother's home town, before he realises that she can't understand a word

ACT III

CONTEXT

'Murren' (p. 54) in English, murrain, refers to a plague, or infectious blight. It is significant in this scene because Bridget later smells in the air the first signs of potato blight. In Irish, Murren derives from Saint Muranus.

- Yolland disappears.
- The Donnelly Twins are suspected.
- The play draws towards a tragic climax.

Yolland is missing, and more soldiers have arrived to search for him. Some of the characters suspect that the Donnelly twins have something to do with his disappearance. The disappearance of an army officer, even one involved only in map-making, would be a serious matter in a country which is resisting the colonising power. Manus is angry from having found out about Maire and Yolland, and is desperate to get away from Baile Beag and to delay taking up his new job in Inis Meadhon. He is obviously upset by what Sarah has told him about Maire and Yolland, and perhaps he needs time to think about his feelings and his future. Lancey's soldiers are already rifling their way through the farms and houses nearby looking for Yolland, and Owen advises Manus not to run away. It is clear that Manus's departure may be taken by Lancey as a sign that he has been involved in Yolland's disappearance, because Manus has a plausible motive for harming Yolland.

But Manus refuses and leaves anyway. He has not, in actual fact, harmed Yolland. He tells Owen that he hurled only an insult at

CHECK THE NET
For details of the Irish potato famine, search **http:// www.bbc.co.uk/ history/state**.

Yolland, who, in any case, didn't understand it because it was in Gaelic. Manus feels that he would have been better to have insulted him in English, at least then Yolland would have understood that it was an act of defiance, rather than an attempt to communicate with him. Manus says that this was 'The wrong gesture in the wrong language' (p. 70), and this echoes his earlier statement that Doalty's trick with the surveyor's pole was 'a gesture … to indicate a presence' (p. 12). Manus has learned now that some gestures are better than others, that gestures, in order to be effective, must be understood. In the phrase 'The lame scholar turned violent' (p. 70) Manus expresses his self-disgust. He is struck by how pathetic he must have seemed with his lame leg, struggling to find Yolland to strike him with a stone. Before he leaves, Manus again coaches Sarah. The scene is similar to the one in Act I, in which Manus urges Sarah to speak properly. Manus is colder towards Sarah now, and seems to interrogate her for her answers rather than help her with her words. His lack of warmth conveys the anger which he is feeling, possibly towards her for being the bearer of bad news. She takes it to mean that she has done something wrong and begins to cry. Manus leaves.

Doalty and Bridget enter with the news that the soldiers have commenced operations throughout Baile Beag. Bridget lets slip that she knows something about what happened to Yolland, as she knows enough to point to the Donnelly twins.

Maire arrives but is distraught with the disappearance of Yolland, and she tells them absent-mindedly of the place names of Yolland's home. She pronounces them as both she and Yolland did with Gaelic names the night before. The place names become like poetry, like Jimmy Jack's Homer. She recalls Yolland's last words to her, 'I'll see you yesterday' (p. 77) as he attempted to speak Gaelic but got 'yesterday' confused with 'tomorrow'. This error is revealing, as it conveys the impression that there are no certainties, no tomorrows, just as Maire and Yolland were confused by the word 'always' (p. 52). In Yolland's confusion of tenses, future with past, he echoes the theme of being trapped in the past. Maire indicated that she has nothing left to do but to embark for America, for Brooklyn in New York.

CONTEXT

When Jimmy Jack mentions the Visigoths, Vandals and Huns on p. 58, he is either making an astute and ironic parallel between English soldiers and barbaric tribes sacking Rome, or he is demonstrating once again that he is trapped in the myths of the past even when soldiers are upsetting his homeland. Visigoths and Vandals were Germanic and the Huns were Asian peoples who invaded former territories of the Roman empire in the fourth and fifth centuries AD.

CONTEXT

The 1798 rebellion in Ireland was planned by a secular Republican organisation, the United Irishmen, inspired and supported by French revolutionaries. They were disorganised and inadequately armed, and were defeated in the summer of that year.

Lancey arrives on the scene, and delivers a series of threats to the class through Owen's translations. He threatens evictions, the destruction of livestock and crops, and the levelling of every house in the area. But resistance to the army's threats has already started, as Doalty notices that the army's camp is on fire.

The play concludes with Hugh facing devastation as he is told that he will not be headmaster at the National School, with Maire lost and confused, and even more desperate to learn English, with Jimmy Jack still wrapped up in the classics, and with Doalty, Bridget and Owen all running after the soldiers, either to resist them or to stop the mayhem caused by them. Hugh drunkenly reminisces on his and Jimmy's abortive attempt to take part in the 1798 rebellion. Jimmy and Hugh were young men, fired with enthusiasm and a romantic idealism inspired by Virgil's *Aeneid*. They did not make it very far, however, deciding to turn back after twenty-three miles. But they manage to make even their cowardice sound heroic, by describing themselves like Ulysses, 'homesick for Athens' (p. 89).

COMMENTARY

Translations reaches its tragic climax. Bridget smells the sweet scent of rotting potato stalks in the air, a prophetic sign of potato famine. Hugh delivers the final speech of the play, in which he tries to recite Virgil's description of how Carthage was destroyed by the Romans, but somehow Hugh cannot remember all the words.

Although there are tensions between the characters in the preceding scenes, relationships between the characters are stable and, for the most part, amicable, until the turbulent and tragic climax in this final Act. Whereas Doalty shows kindness to Yolland earlier in the play, here he feels compelled to respond violently to the actions of the other English soldiers. Manus too feels that he has to resort to desperate measures. Friel is showing us individuals who are drawn into action by changing circumstances. In this case, the event which has precipitated a crisis – the disappearance of Yolland – is outside the control of any of the characters. What Friel does not tell us, and deliberately so, is whether those actions are ethical or moral, or even sensible. He shows his characters performing certain actions, but does not comment on them.

The fragility of human relationships and the futility of communication are the subjects of this final Act. The love between Maire and Yolland was bound to be difficult, given the barriers in language and culture, but their relationship is destroyed by the political antagonisms between the English army and Irish resistance. Manus is consumed with jealousy of Yolland's relationship with Maire, and can only respond pathetically with 'the wrong gesture in the wrong language'(p. 70). Jimmy Jack breaks down in tears, abandoning the pretences of living in his mythical world, and crying to Hugh of the need for companionship. Hugh also is made pathetic by circumstance, knocked from his perch of pomposity and self-conceit, and left unemployed and probably destitute by the new National School. His memory fades, and his final lines suggest that his world is on the brink of destruction.

> **CONTEXT**
>
> 'Edictum imperatoris' (Latin) (p. 52) means the imperial verdict. Even when Owen is trying to convince Hugh that this is not some mythological tale but the real threat of violence which is facing them, Hugh responds in Latin, speaking of the Roman empire.

GLOSSARY

58	**Thermopylae** the site of a famous battle in 480BC where a small army of Spartans temporarily repulsed invading hordes of Persian warriors
61	**like bloody beagles** Doalty is referring to the soldiers, who will chase Manus like hunting dogs, now that he is under suspicion
62	**a wake** the play begins with a christening, and now is coming to an end with a wake, the mourning of the dead
63	**When my grandfather ... without a fight** Doalty knows that there are precedents for the army's actions, and the people of Baile Beag have survived such threats and acts of violence before. He is also certain that he will use violence to resist them

EXTENDED COMMENTARIES

Sadly, it is not possible to reproduce the passages in question within these Notes. You will need to refer to your own copy of the play when reading the analyses.

Four passages have been selected from *Translations* to illustrate different aspects of the play, such as language and style, **characterisation**, staging and performance issues, and recurrent themes and techniques. After an initial indication of the significance of each piece of text, the information will then be given in note form so that you can be guided by suggestions, rather than influenced by essays which espouse a particular point of view.

TEXT 1   ACT I (pp. 1-24)

From: Stage directions to 'MAIRE: I'm talking about...'

Friel began his literary career as a writer of short stories. This craft often emerges in the stage directions, which are as carefully crafted in his plays as the dialogue, and should not be neglected as a source of information about the play.

QUESTION

Do the other implements in the hedge-school (cartwheel, lobster-pots, farming tools, hay, and so forth) suggest any of the main themes of the play?

Setting

The byre (cattle shed) is *'disused'*, the stairs are *'without a banister'*, the implements are *'forgotten'* (p. 1).

The set is embedded with clues about ways of existence that have already passed. The room is comfortless, suggesting that learning brings no physical consolation.

Manus is teaching Sarah how to speak. This is the first reference to communication in the play, and is verbal communication in its most basic form. Manus is concerned with the mechanics of speech, and the production of sound. Sarah is considered mute, but Manus is still teaching her. For a reader of the play, this is the introduction to Manus. It is too easy to see him as a passive character throughout the play. He endures his father's boorish behaviour, and Maire's flirting with Yolland. He refuses to apply for the teaching post because Hugh has. The stage directions correct the impression, and give instead a picture of an intense young man, who works *'with a kind of zeal'* (p. 1). Too often these qualities can be lost in the dialogue, and even in production.

The description of Jimmy Jack places his learning in context. He is a lonely bachelor, but his learning is part of who he is. Without this knowledge it is too easy to see him merely as an eccentric, but he has an organic connection to the classical world, and his interpretation of it is seen very much in terms of his life in Baile Beag.

Characters

Shortly after Hugh, the school master, has returned from a baptism at which he has had a few drinks, he begins to teach his class. He is teaching some of them the **classics** and others how to do arithmetic, but much of his teaching consists of passing on local news to them. The significance of this scene is that it informs us of the imminent arrival of Captain Lancey of the Royal Engineers, and it highlights the controversies surrounding the language issue in the play, by showing us that the characters differ in their attitudes to the English language, in particular. Hugh is scornful of the English language, which, as far as he is concerned, reflects no tradition of learning and honour, and is used only for conducting business (p. 23). To Hugh, who has an aristocrat's aloof attitude to commerce, the English language is base because it is tainted by its material uses. But notice the **irony** of what Hugh says next. He calls for bread, thereby showing that his own language is also used for daily business. Furthermore, his criticism of English for being too commercial comes not long after he has just collected fees from his students. He also shows himself later to be ignorant of one the most famous of English poets, William Wordsworth. Hugh mocks English by suggesting that Gaelic and the classical languages are better suited to each other, and that English is less easy to trace to classical roots. There is irony here too, for, with the play conducted in English, and Hugh constantly asking his students to explain the derivations of Latin words, Friel is showing us that English has a close relationship with the classical languages too, and given the language in which the play is written, Hugh's magisterial assertion: 'English…couldn't really express us' (p. 23) is deeply ironic.

Hugh is clearly in authority. He controls the class by interspersing the information which he wants to impart to them with questions which test their abilities in Latin vocabulary and grammar. He also

CONTEXT

Hugh's gossipy, informal style of teaching contrasts with the formal, stiff style of Lancey's delivery. It is also an emblem of the difference between the largely oral and folksy Irish attitudes, and the organised and trained colonial power that will standardise everything, including places and education.

CHECK THE NET
For a portrait of Daniel O'Connell, see **http://www.rte.ie/news/2002/0907/gallery.html**.

dismisses them quickly for not knowing answers, as he does with Maire when he asks for the Latin for 'acquiesced' (pp. 23-4) and is impatient with pupils who interrupt him or ask awkward questions – 'Well, girl?' (p. 24). He is opinionated and self-assured. He spurns one of the most renowned and admired Irish politicians of his time, Daniel O'Connell, by describing him as 'that little Kerry politician' (p. 24), although, by the time in which the play is set, 1833, O'Connell's reputation was well established throughout Ireland as a barrister and political leader. O'Connell rose to prominence as a campaigner for Catholic emancipation and became known as 'The Liberator'. He was controversial, on the language question, suggesting, as Maire says, that Gaelic was 'a barrier to modern progress' (p. 25).

Hugh also makes confident statements as if they were self-evident truths: 'English...couldn't really express us'. He is preoccupied with his own importance, so much that he shows no interest in major figures such as O'Connell and Wordsworth. He also seems only to admire in other people their willingness to agree with him: 'to his credit he acquiesced to my logic' (p. 23). And he is insensitive to the reactions and feelings of others. The stage directions indicate that he fails to notice how he has hurt Maire with his comments on the English language, and he appears to be unaware of the **irony** of repudiating English as the language of commerce while he shouts for a slice of bread from Manus.

Maire wants to learn the English language, and this leads her into an argument with her school master, who voices his distaste for English as a language of 'commerce' (p. 23) She indicates her disagreement with him first by turning away and remaining silent when he asks a question, and then by interrupting him and challenging his authority. She shows herself to be sufficiently self-confident to take a stand against the authority of the master, although the stage directions tell us that she does this *'uneasily but determinedly'* (p. 24). She is an idealist and a fighter, who is willing to stand up for what she wants. She differs from Doalty and Bridget in that she knows the answers to Hugh's questions, and, rather than knowing gossip about Daniel O'Connell's sexual exploits and his 'scrounging' for votes, she is able to quote from his speeches. She is aware that English will be of better use to her than Greek or Latin, and represents the will to embrace **modernity** as opposed to the master's clinging to **antiquity**.

Doalty is shown in this scene to be surprisingly bright and alert, although just before this Hugh has told him that he knows nothing. It is rare for Doalty to know an answer to one of the master's questions, and here he surprises even himself by being able to answer correctly Hugh's question about the meaning of 'conjugation' (p. 23). He is also aware of the gossip surrounding the politician, Daniel O'Connell. He points out to his fellow pupils that, although O'Connell talks about the necessity of Irish people learning the English language, O'Connell uses the Irish language to solicit votes.

Doalty is shown here to be bright in an unscholarly, gossipy way, then, but also a joker, prodding and winking at Bridget. He may be prodding and winking at her because of the meaning of the word 'conjugation', which can refer to wedding rituals.

Bridget, like Doalty, is a minor character, and is a fair student, but seems to be more interested in what is going on outside class than inside it. She knows the gossip about Daniel O'Connell, too, but she is also conscientious enough to know her Latin grammar. Thus, unlike Doalty, there is no surprise when Bridget knows the answer to the master's questions.

Jimmy Jack is notably docile through this extract, answering the occasional question, until Bridget mentions the sexual activities of Daniel O'Connell. Jimmy is suddenly awake and interested in any mention of sex or women, and throughout the play Jimmy is obsessed with marrying a goddess.

Although Manus is offstage during much of this part of the play, we learn that Manus is mistreated by Hugh, who shouts orders at him and speaks to his own son as if he were his personal slave. It is also apparent that he has a gift for teaching, and is given to helping others.

> **CONTEXT**
>
> As most of the action takes place indoors, the larger picture must be reported by the characters. In classical Greek theatre, this was done by the chorus, who acted as narrator. In this scene, Doalty and Bridget have a function very like the chorus, but Friel clothes their narrative function in the guise of gossip and excitement.

Recurrent themes and techniques

Language is a persistent concern of the play, obviously, and in this scene we see Maire arguing with Hugh that it is the English language which the pupils need to be taught. Hugh teaches them the classical languages of Latin and Greek, while Maire demands to learn English. The difference between them is that Hugh believes that knowing the classical languages is worth while because it cultivates their learning, whereas Maire's approach to education is much more utilitarian. Languages for her are only worth learning when they have a practical purpose in life. Gaelic is also marked out as a language with no practical purpose, and Maire cites O'Connell's argument that Gaelic was hindering Ireland from becoming a modern, industrialised and commercial nation. Hugh contends that Gaelic is the essence of who the Irish people are, and that English couldn't express Irishness. The issue for Maire, however, is that English will help her to advance in life and give her better opportunities, whereas Gaelic will entrap her in impoverished, rural Ireland.

Cultural differences between the English and the Irish, and among the Irish themselves, are suggested in this extract. Hugh represents the English Captain Lancey as a humble but ignorant man, who has no knowledge of the classics and is interested in mere commercial and administrative matters. On the other hand, he implies, the Irish are scholars and are interested in higher cultural and spiritual matters. He is suggesting here an absolute difference between the materialistic English, whose language is appropriate to market trading, and the spiritual Irish, whose language is associated with the learned languages of the ancient Greek and Roman civilisations. Maire then shows that not all the Irish are interested purely in these spiritual and cultural aspects of life. She simply wants to improve her prospects of doing well materially in the world, and for that she needs to learn the English language.

Irony is used twice in this extract as a technique to undermine what Hugh is telling us. The first example is that Hugh claims that English is particularly suited to the 'purposes of commerce' (p. 23), implying that Gaelic is above commercial and material things, but, ironically, he then shouts to Manus for a slice of soda bread,

QUESTION

To what extent are both Manus and Owen outsiders in Baile Beag? How is their alienation from the others similar, and in what ways does it differ? Can any other characters be said to be alienated?

showing us inadvertently that Gaelic is equally used to gain material needs. The second example is that Hugh proposes that Gaelic has a much closer relationship with the classical languages than English, but the irony is that throughout the extract Hugh is asking pupils to explain the Latin roots of *English* words. The relationship between English and Latin is therefore shown to be as close as the relationship between Gaelic and Latin. Both examples of irony work because the language that we are to believe is spoken is Gaelic, whereas in fact the language spoken is English. What the play shows the audience inadvertently is that Gaelic can be a commercial language and that English has very strong roots in Latin.

Languages and style

There are differences in how various characters use language. The clearest example in this extract is between Hugh and Maire. Hugh is highly articulate. If anything, he parades his knowledge of vocabulary before his pupils as if he needed to prove something to them. He uses unusual words such as 'verecund', 'perambulations' and 'conjugation' (p. 23), partly to test his students on their vocabulary, but also to display his own language skills. In contrast, Maire plays down her knowledge of language. She knows exactly what 'perambulations' means, but it is not a word she is ever likely to use. She tends to speak in short sentences which are repetitive: 'That's what my mother says. That's what I say. That's what Dan O'Connell said last month in Ennis' (p. 24). Likewise, one could not imagine Hugh speaking the above lines. The differences between Hugh and Maire in their language use indicates differences in character and attitude. In some ways, Maire is more confident than Hugh. He seems to need to use a more complex, or highly crafted style in language to show that he is a learned man. Instead of saying 'hello' when he enters the school, for example, he says 'Vesperal salutations to you all' (p. 21). This may indicate a defensiveness on Hugh's part, a fear that he must prove that he is learned in ways which are immediately, audibly apparent, particularly as his school is soon to be threatened by the new National School.

Staging

Much of the dramatic tension of *Translations* when it is performed on stage is created out of the contrast between cultural identities and

QUESTION

Friel, in a reply to Andrews in *The Crane Bag* (7.2. 1983) commented: 'You don't go to *Macbeth* for history'. To what extent does art, particularly political art, which *Translations* certainly is on one level, have a duty to reflect the facts of history?

attitudes. Lancey and Hugh differ hugely in temperament, attitudes and values, and their differences form part of the play's tension, which develops into a final destructive climax. Hugh and Maire differ greatly in their attitudes to their own culture, and Maire's demand to know English, and Hugh's refusal to teach her, form part of the tension of the play too. These tensions are presented differently on stage in the play. In this extract, we find out what Lancey represents and how he is opposed to Hugh through the device of Hugh telling the class. By doing it this way, Friel has prepared the audience for Lancey before he appears. No argument need take place between Lancey and Hugh to show us the differences between them, because we have already been presented with information about these differences in the scene extracted above. The contrast between Hugh and Maire, on the other hand, is presented through the device of an argument. The stage directions indicate that Hugh treats Maire indifferently, not noticing her gestures, and making her feel uneasy in challenging his authority. But they also indicate that Maire is capable of being determined and sticking to her demand to be taught English. By using these two very different techniques of staging debate, Friel reserves the more serious clash between the Irish and the English until the final Act, and allows the audience to see a clash with less force, between a 'girl' and her 'master'.

How these two contrasts are performed on stage is crucial. Hugh will remain calm and self-assured at the front of the class, and Maire will, when addressing herself to him, be resolute but nonetheless will appear to be small and powerless. If Hugh refuses, she has very few tricks up her sleeve to achieve her goal. So, the argument between Maire and Hugh has less dramatic power than the potential clash between Hugh and Lancey. Lancey will look like a powerful figure on his arrival, dressed in uniform and ready to dish out instructions to the natives. Hugh looks equally powerful, as an authority in Baile Beag, and as a large man with a walking stick and an articulate commanding voice. A clash between these two would have immense dramatic power, as it would **symbolise** the clash of Gaelic and English authorities. That is why Friel must find ways in staging the play of holding back that clash until the last Act, when Hugh capitulates, of course, and accepts that his own language and culture will yield to English pressure.

QUESTION

To what extent is Hugh just a voice, full of 'sound and fury, signifying nothing'? Does he have any real authority other than that created by his own personality?

TEXT 2   ACT II SCENE 1 (pp. 50–2)

From 'YOLLAND: I mean'…to HUGH's exit

This extract is taken from Act II scene 1, in which Yolland and
Owen have been engaged in filling in the Name-Book with the new
anglicised place names. Hugh disturbs them when he emerges from
upstairs. They begin to talk, and Yolland explains to Hugh his
fascination with all things Irish. Hugh is happy to discuss with him
the richness of Gaelic language and literature, and to advise Yolland
about how to feel less alienated in Baile Beag. Owen gets irritated
by his father's 'pompous' (p.52) talk, and tries to embarrass him.
Hugh then leaves them to their work, and Owen and Yolland
proceed to have an argument about whether or not to change a
Gaelic name to a more anglicised form.

Characters

Hugh is eloquent in his descriptions of the Gaelic language and
literature. He expresses the view that what Irish people lack in
material possessions or wealth, they compensate for in spiritual
and intellectual riches. Although he refers to Yolland throughout
the scene as 'sir' and 'Lieutenant', he seems to be kind and friendly
towards the young English soldier who is so interested in
everything Irish. He explains in a good-natured manner the roots
of Gaelic literature and his own work on language and translation.
He even offers Yolland advice about how to become a part of
their community more fully, in response to Yolland telling him
how isolated he feels from the people of Baile Beag. But there is
also a hint of **irony** in Hugh's descriptions of language and
literature.

QUESTION

Is Hugh's irony his
own, or is Friel
commenting
ironically on both
Hugh and Irish
culture in general?

When he describes the richness of Gaelic literature as 'our only
method of replying to … inevitabilities' (p. 51), for example, is he
not referring to the pressures which English colonialism has put on
the language and culture of the Gaelic-speaking people? The pause
before the word 'inevitabilities' suggests that he is calculating the
effect of a phrase which is critical of English colonialism. Similarly,
with the final sentence in this extract, he calculates the effect in the

same manner. The pause before 'fact' (p. 52), where 'fact' refers to the certain imposition of the English language on the people, may indicate that Hugh is making thinly veiled criticisms of the English soldier for what his uniform represents. On the surface, then, Hugh seems to be benevolent towards the soldier, but perhaps all his comments are laced with criticisms. After all, telling Yolland that a rich literature compensates for material poverty is a clever way of pointing out to him that the people are indeed desperately poor.

Yolland seems to be unaware in this extract of any irony in Hugh's descriptions of Gaelic language and literature, although he does say later that Hugh 'knows what's happening' (p. 52). Yolland instead seems to be like a schoolboy, enthralled by the master's eloquent tales of culture and history. He is deferential and humble before Hugh, and shows a keen interest in learning from the school master. He is bearing the signs of the romantic idealist, the sentimental stage-Englishman, who has fallen hopelessly in love with Baile Beag and its people and is innocent of anything suspicious or critical in their dealings with him.

Owen is embarrassed by his father's 'pompous' statements. He tells Hugh to 'stop that nonsense' (p. 40) perhaps because he realises that Hugh is deliberately playing up before Yolland, or indeed that Hugh is mocking Yolland's sentimentality for Gaelic culture. To prevent Hugh from embarrassing, or criticising, Yolland, Owen decides to embarrass his father by reading out the new names of local places, and showing Hugh that, if Yolland feels alienated from this community, so too, Hugh has been alienated from his own landscape. Owen is, then, trying to steer a middle course between Hugh and Yolland here, and to keep Hugh from making Yolland feel any more 'cut off' from the people than he already does. In doing this, Owen is either making heroic efforts to reconcile the two cultures, English and Irish, by protecting Yolland from feeling alienated, or he is betraying his own people in order to please his English friends.

Recurrent themes and techniques

The people of Baile Beag are in a state of transition from one language and culture to another, and Hugh is reflecting on what

CHECK THE BOOK
Read Tony Corbett, 2002 for his interesting views on the linguistic concerns of Friel's plays. See **Further reading**..

such change means. He explains that Gaelic society believes that its cultural traditions and its language are immemorial, that they have endured unaltered for centuries, possibly even millennia. Its place names seem to reflect the permanence of the natural features of the landscape or traditional elements of Gaelic lifestyles. Faced with this sense of a long tradition and culture which is alien to him, Yolland seems overcome with awe and admiration. But Hugh tells him that he must by all means try to learn the Gaelic language so that he doesn't feel so alienated from the people, but that words are only 'signals, counters. They are not immortal' (p. 52). Hugh tells Yolland that it might be worth learning Gaelic, but not to worry too much as it looks as though everybody in Baile Beag might be speaking English soon in any case. This sense of transition is important throughout the play, but here Hugh hints that there is something already present in Gaelic culture which may precipitate change anyway: 'it can happen that a civilisation can be imprisoned in a linguistic contour which no longer matches the landscape of … fact' (p. 52). Hugh is suggesting here that a culture which has based itself on the strength of its **antiquity** is not prepared for a giant leap into the modern world, and that is the challenge facing Gaelic society in 1833, and indeed Northern Irish society in 1980.

CHECK THE BOOK
If you know little of Irish history, look at Robert Kee's *Ireland: A History*, 1980, based on the BBC/RTE television series, which is full of interesting details, and has a chronology and numerous illustrations.

Irony is evident in Hugh's descriptions of the richness of the vocabulary and literature of Gaelic. The Irish people may spend all their energies on the beauties and complexities of their language, but what Hugh also makes clear is that, if the language which they speak has become redundant, then they have wasted their efforts. Gaelic may possess 'a syntax opulent with tomorrows' (p. 51). but as Hugh then suggests, the language itself might not have any tomorrows.

Language and style

Hugh is calm and confident in the way he expresses himself, whereas Yolland is more excited and defers to Hugh's authority. This difference between them is evident in the manner of their speech. Hugh's speech is articulate and self-assured. He speaks in sentences which are, for the most part, well constructed and premeditated. He pauses, it seems, only for effect, before he says a

**CHECK
THE BOOK**
*The Oxford
Companion to Irish
History*, ed. S.J.
Connolly, 1998,
contains entries on
key historical events
and can be useful in
finding out more
about the
background history
to *Translations*.

word which he wants to emphasise. And despite the fact that Owen mocks him for being absent-minded, Hugh is masterful in his control of language. Yolland is less than masterful, however. He changes direction in the middle of a sentence – 'And your Gaelic literature – you're a poet yourself' (p. 50). He also stammers with excitement – 'It – it – it's really astonishing' (p. 50) These are the means by which Friel communicates the relationship between the two characters.

Similarly, the differences between Hugh and Owen are illustrated by the ways in which they both speak. Hugh is eloquent and long-winded, almost pompous in his speech. He utters abstract ideas – 'We like to think we endure around truths immemorially posited' (p. 50). Owen, on the other hand, is direct and simple. He counters his father's eloquence by asking him to 'stop that nonsense'. He speaks in short, uncomplicated sentences, unlike his father.

Staging

The degree of irony, mockery, bitterness or sarcasm in this scene will depend on how it is performed by each of the actors. Hugh's facial gestures and his tone of voice will alter how the audience interprets the scene. If his intention is to remind Yolland that he is part of the colonial destruction of Gaelic culture, how might he look and sound when he says the word 'inevitabilities' (p. 51)? If he is mocking the ridiculous notion that the Irish enjoy their poverty because they're a spiritual people, perhaps he would sneer or raise his eyebrows when he tells Yolland that 'you could call us a spiritual people' (p. 50). Does Yolland realise that he is being mocked or criticised by Hugh? How might he make his awareness apparent on stage? He might nod and smile at Hugh at the words 'inevitabilities' and 'fact', indicating that he knows what Hugh is referring to. Yolland might not be so sentimental and naïve as he appears to be, and might indicate by facial gestures that he is capable of understanding the '**subtexts**' or implications of what Hugh is saying. These are some of the issues of interpretation which might affect a performance of the play.

TEXT 3 ACT II SCENE 2

The entire scene

This short scene, in which Yolland and Maire have come away from a dance together is in some ways a touchstone of the play as a whole. Here we have all the themes in microcosm: translation, clash of cultures, **alienation**, fresh use of stereotypes, love and conflict. Here we have Friel's art poured into very few pages, which are replete with the playwright's skill and favourite stage techniques.

The theatrical conceit

Friel used this term to describe the technique he uses of having the *actors* all speaking English, but the *characters* speaking a mixture of English and Gaelic. In technical terms, this is a difference between the dramatic text (the written page) and the performance text (the actual staging of the play).

The conceit is focused on this scene. In Act I scene 1, Friel makes it clear that the people of Baile Beag use Gaelic as their everyday language. This is done with very broad strokes, using the comic figure of Lancey, with his stereotypical English attitude to foreigners (not speaking English = low intelligence). It also introduces Maire and Yolland as a potential couple, and Yolland's 'Sorry – sorry?' (p. 35) as an indication that he does not understand. This marker is repeated three times in Act II scene 1 (pp. 59–60), so that by the time it is needed, the audience is thoroughly familiar with the convention.

For the first ten lines or so of Act II scene 2, one could be forgiven for thinking that Maire and Yolland are speaking the same language. A careful reading reveals that Friel is using one of his most effective techniques: two distinct lines of dialogue which sound superficially like conversation. Maire and Yolland are not speaking to each other, they speak in parallel. Their conversation is similar because their physical and emotional situation is identical. At first they are awkward with each other. Maire is embarrassed at being alone with Yolland, and says to him 'Manus'll wonder where I've got to' (p. 62). They cannot understand each other's language, but their

CHECK THE BOOK

Keir Elam's *The Semiotics of Theatre and Drama*, Methuen 1984, while a very dense text, contains some very important tools for dissecting the problems of plays, both on the page and on the stage, including a useful and complete definition of dramatic and performance texts.

looks and movements must suggest that they are attracted to each other. In this extract Yolland and Maire find a way of communicating their affection for each other through the sound of the place names. This brings them together, they caress and kiss, but the scene continues with Sarah watching them kissing before running off to tell Manus.

Characters

In Act III, when Yolland has gone missing, Maire recalls their romantic evening together, and how he made some mistakes in Gaelic, telling her 'I'll see you yesterday' (p. 77). In this scene, however, Yolland's pronunciation of Gaelic place names is perfect, and it is his enthusiasm for Maire, for the language, and for the place which is conveyed to the audience. Yolland has fallen in love with all three, and what we witness in this scene is how much he wants to belong to Baile Beag. He is indeed an enthusiastic hibernophile, as Owen remarks of him in Act I. Yolland wants to live with Maire in Baile Beag and to be able to communicate with her, but the only way he can do that at this stage is to recite place names. **Ironically**, he knows these place names so well because he is involved in eradicating them.

Maire is nervous of her feelings for Yolland and appears to be embarrassed and shy. But when he speaks the names of the surrounding villages and townlands of her home, she is moved by them and responds to Yolland. She is clearly in love with him, and wants to run away with him to other places. Maire is desperate to get out of Baile Beag, and part of her dream to escape now involves Yolland. She is tender towards him, and seems to understand his desperation to fit in with the local community. She is depicted here as sensitive and emotional, a romantic idealist, who is willing to put at risk her relationship with Manus for a dream and a man with whom she has fallen in love but about whom she knows very little other than his daily routine.

Recurrent themes and techniques

The possibility of communication and its fundamental unreliability are crucial elements in the scene. When Lancey or Yolland speaks to

CONTEXT

This is the only scene which takes place outside the hedge-school, and the only one in which the representatives of the conflicting cultures are in harmony with each other. It is possible that the byre itself is a **symbol** of the entrapment of Irish culture, and of its inability to change.

the Irish characters, for the most part they need Owen to translate for them. This is acceptable for official business, but Yolland wishes to communicate his private feelings to Maire. An interpreter would hardly be appropriate, so Yolland must find a way of communicating to a woman when they do not have a language in common. When he speaks her name she does not respond, but, in the Gaelic place names of the area around Baile Beag, Yolland finds a language which she can speak too. They move closer together, each speaking but apparently in different languages, until they do seem to be able to understand each other. They speak towards the end of this scene as if they understood every word spoken by each other. And it is this 'as if' which is important. Yolland and Maire may be overcoming the linguistic and cultural barrier, and finding a method of discourse, or they may be deluded. After all, there is not much actual communication, in the pedestrian sense, going on. They merely use the sounds as a cloak for their embarrassment before they kiss. Although an audience may feel that there is real communication going on, in reality there is not. Friel may be writing a scene in which there is hope for true communication between cultures, or he may be writing a scene in which the audience is tricked into believing that this kind of communication is possible. Typically, with Friel, there is not enough information in the scene to allow one to come to any conclusion.

There are also hints of potential disagreements, which the language barrier prevents from becoming apparent. Yolland wants to stay in Baile Beag, whereas Maire is intent on getting out of the village. As Yolland seems to love the place as much as he loves Maire, and as Maire talks throughout the play of leaving Baile Beag, this is bound to cause tension between them. The limited means which they have of communicating with each other prevents this tension from surfacing, however.

The significance of place names is apparent in this scene, as it is evident in debates and arguments elsewhere in the play. Through a recitation of the Gaelic names, Yolland apparently finds a way of communicating with Maire. It is particularly the exotic sound of those names which must appeal to the English-speaking audience as a kind of poetry. In translation, they are hardly romantic or poetic

CONTEXT

Languages divide the world differently, and therefore perceive reality in slightly different ways. Gaelic, for example, has a Continuous Present tense, used nominally to describe habitual events, but inexpressible in English without twisting grammar and syntax. The Continuous Present of 'téigh', to go, is 'téim', roughly translatable as 'I do be going'. The idea of a continuous (unchanging) present is relevant to *Translations*, in that the seemingly unchanged lives of the inhabitants of Baile Beag are about to be transformed, partly by having the Continuous Present taken away from them.

CONTEXT

In Gaelic literature the recital and explanation of place names, known as *dinnseanchas*, carries an almost mystical significance. Yolland and Owen, in Act II scene 1, had already discussed the meaning of some of the names. Here they are recited like a mantra.

at all: mouth of the river, black ridge, hole of the sheep, fort of Maol, fort of the foreigner, and so on. Only in the strangeness of the language do the names have any poetic or romantic significance, just as Maire will recite the names of English villages – 'Winfarthing, Barton Bendish, Saxingham Nethergate' (p. 78) – for the same poetic effect which comes of not knowing their meaning. However, in this scene, conventional meaning is less important than constructed meaning and the sound of the words. By constructed meaning, I mean that the words are used for a different purpose. They are used to express love, to be a carrier for a particular tone. Maire and Yolland map out a topography which brings them, briefly, together. It is similar to listening to a lovesong in a foreign language: one is aware of the general intention, but not the specific meanings. Using place names, Friel has constructed a love-duet which is highly artificial, highly theatrical and which can be highly effective on stage.

Ironically, the kiss at the end of the scene is witnessed by Sarah, who uses her new-found ability to tell Manus. In a very classical turn, Manus is the source of his own adversity. If he had not taught Sarah to speak, she might not have been able to tell him, and his acceptance of the post on Inis Meadhon might not have been so precipitous.

Language and style

The sound of the Gaelic language gives this scene its poetic tone for non Gaelic-speaking audiences. Yolland and Maire pick up on the sounds of the names. When Yolland says 'Lis na nGall', Maire follows with 'Lis na nGradh' (pp. 65–6). There is no particular reason why she should do so. This is one part of the play where the structure shows through. Friel needs to begin the recitation, and so simply puts a similar, but different place name into Maire's mouth. By the repetition of 'Lis' and the 'ng' sound, a rhythm is created. They continue by repeating 'carraig', 'loch', 'machaire' and 'cnoc'. The rhythm changes and becomes more urgent with the final four names: 'Mullach, Port, Tor, Lag' (p. 66).

There is also in this scene an interesting difference between Yolland's expressions of love and Maire's. She tends to express her feelings by describing his body – 'Soft hands', 'your arms are long and thin', and 'the skin on your shoulders is very white'. But Yolland expresses more subjective feelings – 'I spend my days either thinking of you or gazing up at your house' and 'I would tell you how beautiful you are' (p. 66). This reverses the way that they have spoken to each other about the wet grass earlier in the scene, when Maire was expressing subjective feelings about the grass and Yolland was describing objectively the condition of the grass.

Staging

Tone, movement and gesture play a crucial part in communicating the feelings of Yolland and Maire in this scene, and on stage their movements must be choreographed perfectly to respond to certain words and gestures. They move closer as the poetry of names becomes more intense, until they are face to face and touching each other when they have finished reciting the shorter names. Although Maire's descriptions of Yolland may sound detached and unromantic – e.g. 'your arms are long and thin' (p. 66) – they are holding hands, and the tone in which they speak and the gestures which they make can alter how the audience interprets their words. Gestures also form a common language for Maire and Yolland. When Maire says 'You're trembling', Yolland responds and says 'Yes, I'm trembling because of you' (p. 67) Presumably, some gesture has been made by Maire which indicates that she refers to his trembling hands. The staging of the parallel conversations is difficult. The tones and gestures must be precise enough to convey the fact that they do not understand each other's words, but close enough for the audience to understand that their speech is related and their meanings coincide. The lighting is also important in conveying the atmosphere of the scene. The stage directions at the beginning advise that the lighting indicate that the scene is outside, and that the barn is concealed by darkness. This would envelop the two in a moonlight effect, perhaps, with darkness surrounding, thereby creating a sense of intimacy between Maire and Yolland and a sense of insularity protecting them from the world outside. That sense of insularity is, of course, broken at the end of the scene when Sarah enters to see them kissing.

CONTEXT

Mullach means a summit or a mountain-top, Port is a harbour, but also an earthwork; Tor is a tower (also a bush) and Lag is a hollow, a pool in a stream, or, as an adjective means 'weak'. Even the place names chosen by Friel in his poetic litany show the slippage of language, the meanings, divorced from their contexts, are difficult to pin down. This is part of the theme of *Translations*.

TEXT 4 ACT III (pp. 79-91)

From 'LANCEY enters'…to the end of the play

The play is now rushing towards its conclusion. The events set in motion by Yolland and Maire's relationship are now beyond the control of any individual, and will, most likely, lead to the destruction of Baile Beag and the scattering of its inhabitants. Lancey has given the order, and unless Yolland is found, evictions will begin. Jimmy and Hugh are now, for the first time in the play, actually drunk. It is as if a slow degeneration were taking place in Hugh, from the bumptious and opinionated master in Act I to a sad drunk contemplating the past, both his own and that of classical antiquity.

Characters

Lancey is a very different character from the figure of fun that was paraded in Act I. Here he is the crisp, efficient imperial servant, executing standard procedures in the face of civil unrest and resistance. He becomes in this scene a ruthless commander, determined to punish the whole community because someone has harmed or hidden Yolland. His speech incorporates military terminology, referring to the townland as 'this entire section' (p. 81) as if it has already lost some of the humanity that made it a home. In a way, Lancey is the voice of the new order in Baile Beag, a voice that is standardised, dehumanised and English.

Owen's loyalties are tried in the course of the play. In Act I he was able to refer lightly to the cultural *milieu* of Baile Beag as a 'quaint, archaic tongue' (p. 30) without realising the significance of what he was saying. In Act II scene 1 he and Yolland translate the place names into English, here, he translates them back into Irish as Lancey lists the areas for eviction. The same place names which sounded poetic when spoken by Maire and Yolland now take on an elegiac tone, as they are fated to disappear from the map.

Bridget and Doalty have had the function throughout the play as an index of ordinary thought. They represent the feelings and thoughts of the populace in general. In Act I the soldiers are the victims of

QUESTION

To what extent are Bridget and Doalty representative of ordinary people during civil unrest? They are a-political, and lack understanding of the bigger picture, but they 'go along' with the actions of others. Is Friel making a comment on the relationship between ignorance and violence?

Doalty's prank with the surveyor's pole. By Act III he is, if not complicit in some of the reprisals against the soldiers, at least aware of those who are. Although Doalty is excited by the news that he brings, the arrival of the soldiers is sinister, for they are already beginning to destroy crops and stores in their search for Yolland. The earlier romanticism of the play has now gone. Yolland may have been sentimental about Ireland, and may have fallen in love with an Irish woman and Irish place names, but he was also an officer in the English army. The soldiers are demonstrating their power to destroy as a reminder of what military presence represents. Both Bridget and Doalty are over-excited by the activities of the soldiers, without realising, perhaps, that they will soon be the victims of it. Instead, they are carried along by the tide of unrest.

Jimmy Jack Cassie also reaches the end of his theatrical usefulness here. Friel used him in the early sections of the play to show how natural and unaffected learning had become in the hedge schools. His elderly bachelor's obsession with sex was laughable in Act I, but now becomes pathetic as the two strands come together, and he claims he is about to marry Athene. The confusion and turmoil of the last few days have driven Jimmy back into his stories, into an imaginary landscape in which he can feel safe, as the real landscape around him is brutally changed.

Hugh is the most changed, because he sees more clearly than anyone else what the ordnance survey is doing to the topography of his locality. It can be seen that Friel is using Hugh in the end of the play to make many points on the nature of language and culture, and how they relate to each other. It is a measure of Friel's art that he can fit these seamlessly into the narrative, making them appear to arise from the context. Owen, taking the Name-Book from Hugh, can still claim that it is '…only a catalogue of names', to which Hugh replies gnomically, 'I know what it is' (p. 87). Hugh sees not a mere artefact, or a report, but how the changes in language will alter the landscape, because they will alter the mindset of the people.

His comment: 'We must learn where we live' (p. 88) is resonant in a number of ways. On the literal level, he is coming to terms with the new reality. Whereas Doalty is planning to resist the English army

> **CONTEXT**
>
> Athene's origins are interesting. 'Metis from Hellespont' (p. 88) was the wife of Jupiter (Zeus) who was eaten by him when Jupiter feared that she would bear a child more cunning than him. When Vulcan opened up Jupiter's head, Pallas Athene was born.

when they come to evict him, Hugh is planning to comply with
what the army wants, hoping to appease the new order in Baile Beag
by learning the new English names. On another level, he realises
that he must *learn his place*. The Hugh who was of such significance
in Baile Beag, will not enjoy the same stature in Ballybeg. Similarly,
his new consent to teaching Maire English accepts that English is
part of the new reality of their lives. For this reason he dismisses the
word 'always' (p. 90) as silly. Given that the world around him is
under threat, and faces a new language and culture, the concept of
permanence cannot be anything but ridiculous.

Hugh tries to remember the opening of Virgil's *Aeneid* ('*Urbs
antiqua fuit ...*' – pp. 90–1) but he cannot remember it fully and has
to recite it again. The passage he is quoting is the prophecy of the
destruction of Carthage by the Romans. Carthage was a city on the
north African coast. Hugh is, perhaps, thinking of a parallel
between the destruction of Baile Beag by the English and the
destruction of Carthage by the Romans. The **irony** of Virgil's
Aeneid is that it contains the prophecy of Carthage's tragic
destruction but is written in the language of those who destroyed it.

> **CONTEXT**
>
> Friel is quoting
> very selectively
> from Virgil. *'Urbs
> antiqua fuit'* is
> from line 12, *'late
> regem belloque
> superbum'* is the
> second half of line
> 21. Friel runs them
> together to make
> the context more
> relevant to the
> end of the play.

PART THREE

CRITICAL APPROACHES

CHARACTERISATION

'REPRESENTATIVE' CHARACTERS

The characters in *Translations* are all, in some way, charismatic and believable. Each has her or his own particular traits and habits, and the play contains some very skilful and entertaining characters, including Hugh, Jimmy Jack, Doalty, Yolland and Maire. Their qualities are constructed through dress, dialogue and action, sometimes in the simplest of gestures. They are also, however, in some way, representative of particular views and beliefs, and are variations on recognisable stereotypes. All the characters represent different aspects of the same political process – the transformation of an antiquated Gaelic society into a modern British colony.

The characters may also be presented in terms of their linguistic allegiances: Sarah, who, at the beginning of the play, cannot speak at all; Jimmy Jack, who is lost in classical languages and stories; Maire, who wants to learn English in order to emigrate. Hugh refuses to teach English, and rarely speaks it; Owen's knowledge of Irish and English is a tool to be used; Yolland and Lancey are linguistically isolated in the play because they cannot speak Gaelic; and Manus, who speaks all the languages used in the play, but is ill-at-ease in any of them (Corbett 2002, pp. 22–3). He is an outsider in his own home, as all of Baile Beag will be by the end of the play, linguistically and physically, by reason of the anglicisation of names and Lancey's evictions.

Lancey and Yolland represent the English officials and soldiers who administer and police the changes. They also symbolise different attitudes among the English colonisers: some who regard Ireland without any emotion whatsoever (Lancey), and others who sentimentalise Ireland as an exotic and romantic place (Yolland). The Donnelly twins, whom we never see, represent those who are opposed violently to British rule in Ireland. Manus, Doalty and Bridget seem to represent people who are sympathetic towards

CONTEXT

It is a familiar structure used in movies and television, as well as on the stage, to arrange for a group of different characters to be confined in a small space, and to play out the interaction and conflict of their opinions. In *Translations*, the hedge-school performs a similar function for, although the characters are not strictly confined within it, most of the action takes place within its walls.

violent resistance to British rule, but who become involved directly themselves only when they are forced by circumstance. They may represent the majority of any population, who are politically indifferent until it touches them specifically, or who are swayed by the passion of a small group of extremists. Initially, Owen, the interpreter between the soldiers and the people, seems to border on being a traitor, but towards the end of the play he appears to regret having played this role. Hugh, and more particularly Jimmy Jack, are symbolic of the mindset trapped in romanticising the past and oblivious partly to the events of the present. Hugh is also like Yolland and Maire, however, in symbolising the capacity to open one's mind and heart to other cultures and lifestyles. The love between Yolland and Maire, even if it is doomed to fail, represents the possibility for peace between two nations or cultures by their willingness to learn about and love one another's values and customs. It represents the possibility of communication without language, which carries a cultural baggage that cannot be avoided. The language of gesture and sound worked for Maire and Yolland in the short term. It presents possibilities, but does not offer a simple solution.

CHECK THE BOOK
Friel has a great interest in the way conflict arises through language. His play *Faith Healer*, for example, consists of four contradictory monologues spoken separately by three characters. In this play the conflict has been removed from the physical domain, and happens between the versions of the stories.

Broadly speaking, then, these characters represent a spectrum of possible political positions and ideals which might be as useful in the context of Ireland in 1980 as they are of Ireland in 1833. It is the relationships between these characters, and the various positions which they adopt in relation to each other, that produce the tensions and movement of the play. Manus's response to the fledgling relationship between Maire and Yolland is part of the tension of the play's final act, while the knowledge that Hugh's life as a schoolmaster and a scholar might be drawing to a miserable end fuels the audience's suspense. The tension of the play comes from its human relationships rather than from its action. For example, much more could have been made of Yolland's disappearance to build up the audience's interest, whereas we do not even find out what happens to Yolland. This could be a criticism of the play, or it might indicate that Friel is directing our attention not to the single individual acts of violence but to the wider set of human relationships.

STAGE ENGLISH, STAGE IRISH

English drama in the eighteenth century frequently utilised the stage-Irishman as a comic device, displaying a propensity for **malapropisms**, nonsensical thought, heavy drinking and quarrelsomeness. His weaknesses and perverse logic served to confirm English audiences in their superiority and congratulate them for their sense, rationality and civilised manners. Even in Irish plays written in English, the stereotypical Irishman remains a stock figure. The plays of John B. Keane, a contemporary of Friel, are replete with miserly farmers, scheming matchmakers and tyrannical parents.

In Irish drama of the twentieth century a number of playwrights have sought to dispel the stage-Irishman, most notably George Bernard Shaw in *John Bull's Other Island*, which features a stage-Irishman who is revealed to be a Glaswegian and who plays up the stage-Irish image to make money from English audiences. There also developed in Irish drama the stage-Englishman as a counter to the stage-Irishman.

The stage-Englishman took two forms, both of which are found in Friel's *Translations*. The first is the 'stiff upper-lip' type Englishman who is cold, superrational and reserved, but who is capable of great brutality. Captain Lancey represents this figure in *Translations*. The second is the Englishman who is an enthusiastic and sentimental devotee of anything Irish, and who becomes a figure of fun for Irish audiences because he refuses to acknowledge any of the realities or difficulties of life in Ireland. Lieutenant Yolland is such a figure in Friel's play. He decides that he would like to stay in Ireland because 'It's really heavenly' (p. 45) and cries out on drinking poteen that it is 'Bloody, bloody, bloody marvellous!' (p. 61).

Friel takes these stereotypes, as he does in all his plays, and adapts them to his purposes. In this way we recognise the tradition, and are entertained by the skilful manner in which Friel changes them. For example, Hugh is a stereotypical pompous schoolmaster, full of his own importance and ready to humiliate his pupils. He is also the stereotypical drunken Irishman. He has an additional layer of **irony**

CHECK THE BOOK

Friel has written a short adaptation of an eighteenth-century play by Charles Macklin, (*The True-Born Irishman*) which he titled *The London Vertigo*. It is about the desire 'to metamorphose oneself, to change everything utterly'. Macklin specialised in a kind of stage-Irish humour written for English audiences.

for Irish audiences, as his casual placing of Gaelic literature above Latin is not a-typical of some those who seek to restore the Gaelic language by making grandiose claims for it. But Hugh is also the one who sees more clearly than anyone else the way in which the ordnance survey is a turning point for his way of life. This makes him appear more life-like, and also avoids making him merely a figure of fun. Yolland is the sentimental romantic, falling in love with the unspoiled Gaelic world, but he is also the colonial servant who looks for intelligence on the Donnelly twins. This piece of information saves him from being a one-dimensional saccharine creation.

CONVERTS OR TRADUCERS?

Lancey and the Donnelly twins are on opposite extremes of the political spectrum, and seem to be determined in getting their way through the use of physical force. But there are a number of characters in *Translations* who are willing to embrace other cultures and beliefs. Owen is an early example in the play when he arrives with the English soldiers as their interpreter, and he is an enthusiastic participant in the job of anglicising the place names of his homeland. Hugh, towards the play's end, resigns himself to the inevitability of English becoming the language of the people, and of Gaelic culture declining in importance. Maire and Yolland are perhaps the play's best examples of characters who are willing to give up the customs, language and beliefs in which they have been brought up, to convert to an alternative culture. The play is ambiguous as to how we are to interpret and identify these characters, however. Are they converts, to be admired for their capacity to embrace another culture? Or are they traducers, who abandon the love and warmth of their own culture and betray it to another?

Yolland, for example, in his enthusiasm for all things Irish, does not contradict or dispute any of Hugh's slanderous criticisms of English culture, and seems to give up any loyalty he might have had to his home. And yet he has enough love for his homeland to describe in intimate detail to Maire its landscape and place names. So too, Owen is willing to abandon names and customs which have been part of his family's and his community's history and culture for

CONTEXT

The attitudes in *Translations* are emblematic of the troubled relationship between Ireland and England. Many Irish attitudes are so polarised that to admit value in anything English is seen as disloyal.

centuries, but shows in his own story of the name of 'Tobair Vree' (p. 53) that he has an intimate knowledge of that history and culture. The issue of whether these characters are converts or traducers is particularly important with the Irish characters.

It may be possible that Owen, Maire and Hugh are the realists in the play, who are willing to compromise parts of their own culture in order to gain peace and reconciliation with those from other cultures. They might also be simply looking for a quiet life for themselves, without any thought of the wider implications of their individual actions. It is equally possible that they are the vandals in the play, whose weakness in failing to defend their own culture results in its destruction and slander. This issue is also important in relation to the critical reception of the play, particularly in Ireland. Irish culture is, politically, used to differentiate the Irish from the English. The Gaelic revival of the early part of the twentieth century, and the structures of government and the civil service of the early state expended much energy in this task. Extreme republicans, therefore, would not see any virtue in Manus, Maire or Owen, but see them as traitors. Non-Irish commentators might wonder what the fuss is about. This, in itself, is one of the concerns of the play – the relativism of cultural integrity.

HUGH IN ACT II SCENE 1

In many ways, Hugh Mor O'Donnell is the real protagonist of the play. He represents a static, inward-looking, self-satisfied way of life, whose response to modern outside influences is to ignore them. His chauvinistic attitude to Irish and classical culture and denigration of everything English can be played on stage as comic or **ironic**. They are comical if one considers that Hugh believes what he is saying – that Irish literature was superior to both English and Latin. When he comments that he dabbles in verse, but 'only in Latin' (p. 50), he is suggesting that he considers writing in Latin less prestigious than writing in Gaelic.

His attitude takes on an extra layer of irony if he is aware of the absurdity of his own pompous opinions. One gets the impression that Hugh is sensitive to the fragility of his culture and his position within it, and is shoring it up with a mound of orotund verbiage.

CONTEXT

The discussion between Yolland and Owen on Tobair Vree is a typical piece of Friel's writing. His plays frequently contain questions such as this, which communicate the historical choices facing individuals at a particular time. These questions tend not to be answered, which leaves the issue open for debate. In this instance, Yolland and Owen have the choice to change the name, thereby participating in the destruction of Gaelic culture, or to keep the old name, thereby taking a stand against the process of anglicising Ireland. Friel is revealing the extent to which individuals do have some control over their own local destinies, albeit limited and partial.

CONTEXT

The assertion that Gaelic literature surpassed that of Rome is nothing short of ludicrous. The eighteenth and nineteenth centuries did indeed produce some of the finest Gaelic poetry, the best of which is comparable with the literatures of any culture, but the *corpus* is quite small.

His explanation in Act II scene 1 (p. 50) that he does not know of English literature can only be true if it is a deliberate, studied ignorance, the only response a powerless people can have to colonial occupation. Granted, when he tells Yolland that his people feel closer to southern than to northern Europe, this was largely true for the west coast of Ireland. Traditionally, the region had trading links with Spain, southern France and even Italy, while it was the east of Ireland which had associations with Scotland, Wales, England and northern France. But it is probable that Hugh is also teasing Yolland, and exaggerating his own ignorance, when he says dismissively, 'We tend to overlook your island' (p. 50). After all, by 1833 the British colonial influence in the world was paramount. By referring to it as 'your island', he is engaging in a reductio ad absurdum, reducing the importance of, specifically, the English to that of islanders.

Hugh is also, Friel tells us in the stage directions, deliberately **parodying** himself. Therefore, when he suggests that the people of Gaelic Ireland feel that they live in a timeless world of certainties and 'truths', where nothing changes and the landscape is brimming with the signs of ancient, prehistoric life, one needs to approach it with a sense of the ironies that Friel is constructing. This is particularly the case when, shortly after his speech about spirituality and poverty, he tries to borrow half-a-crown from Owen. This technique of building up an expectation and then destroying it comically is known as **bathos**. The speech beginning: 'A rich language. A rich literature...' (p. 50), appears to state a self-evident truth, that the Irish people lived in greater poverty than the English, or most of Europe, particularly in the eighteenth and early nineteenth centuries, but produced a wealth of literature. Hugh appears to suggest that, in the face of physical hardship, Irish people turn to less material pursuits, and more to spiritual devotion or literary innovation. Yet within moments Friel undercuts the statement: 'Yes, it is a rich language, Lieutenant, full of the mythologies of fantasy and hope and self-deception – a syntax opulent with tomorrows' (p. 51). Friel uses the same phrase 'a rich language' to draw attention to the technique. Hugh implies that the response of the Irish to oppression may be, not spirituality, but a form of self-deluding withdrawal, leading not to spiritual richness but a cultural dead-end. This leads him to one of the most quoted lines in the play: 'it can happen that a civilisation can be imprisoned in a linguistic contour which no longer matches the landscape of…fact' (p. 52). This is a remarkable statement by Hugh, that a language can cease to reflect the way in which people live. It may indicate that Hugh knows that the Gaelic language is no longer meeting the requirements of its people, as Maire has suggested earlier in the play when she quotes from Daniel O'Connell that the Gaelic language is a 'barrier to modern progress' (p. 25). Hugh is, at this point, enunciating Friel's theories on the relationship between people, language and landscape, theories which change and develop with each play. Changing the names of the landscape changes the way in which the speakers of language relate to it. Renaming Irish places with English names makes those places more amenable to English speakers, and less comfortable for the native Irish. The line: 'I am a barbarian in this place because I am not understood by anyone' (p. 85) suggests that barbarians are always defined by the people to whom they are strangers. Barbarian doesn't necessarily mean that they are lacking in culture or intelligence, but means simply that their values are not shared by other tribes or races. Thus barbarism becomes a cultural relativism, and civilisation is defined by the winners. Hugh knows what his culture is about to lose. He resumes his meditation on language and civilisation, begun with Yolland in Act II scene 1: 'It is not the 'facts' of history that shape us, but images of the past embodied in language' (p. 88).

In other words, the facts of history are not important, merely what comes to us from the past through language. Words, as Hugh has taught his pupils throughout the play, contain in them the history of the roots of a civilisation, but that history may or may not be true.

THEMES

ALIENATION

Almost all the characters appear to experience **alienation** in some way. Lancey is alienated as a foreigner in a country for which he appears to have no affection or understanding. Yolland tells Hugh that he feels cut off from the people and he is frustrated by being

**CHECK
THE BOOK**
Friel tells a story in which he recalls fishing with his father, and the walk to and from the lake, and then remembers: 'There's something wrong here…There is no lake along that muddy road. And, since there is no lake, my father and I never walked back from it in the rain…The fact is a fiction. Have I imagined the scene then? Or is it a composite of two or three different episodes? The point is: I don't think it matters…For some reason the mind has shuffled the pieces of verifiable truth and composed a truth of its own' (Delaney, *Brian Friel in Conversation*, 2000, pp. 98–108).

unable to communicate freely with them. Owen displays some feelings of alienation from Baile Beag on his return. He is dressed differently and does not seem to fit in with life in Baile Beag any more. One might ask of the other characters if they feel comfortable and at home in Baile Beag, particularly as many of them seem to be pursuing means of escape. Maire is desperate to emigrate from the village. Jimmy Jack escapes from whatever feelings of loneliness he might have through his classical poetry. Hugh escapes through drinking heavily and by entertaining several myths and images of himself which are exaggerated. Manus is what Seamus Deane has called the 'Frielian outsider', although in relation to *Translations* he applies the term to Owen. The Frielian outsider is one who is, to a large extent, a displaced person in his/her own place. (Deane, 1984: 21). Neither Manus nor Owen are part of the continuum that runs from Doalty to the Donnelly twins, nor still part of the continuum that runs from Lancey to Yolland.

The act of translating Gaelic names into English might be interpreted as an attempt by the English characters to feel more comfortable in Ireland, by making the names less foreign and strange to them. But, if this is so, it succeeds in estranging the local people from their own homes. Hugh is asked by Owen if he will be able to find his way around his own locality now that the names have changed, and Maire sets out for somewhere towards the end of the play but gets lost and returns. These are signs that the local people have been alienated from their own community.

TRANSLATION

The theme of translation is prevalent throughout the play. Hugh constantly asks his pupils to translate from Greek or Latin into Irish. Jimmy Jack translates from Greek into Irish. Owen translates Lancey's English into Irish, and translates Irish place names into English for Yolland. These are examples of linguistic translation. But Friel was influenced by George Steiner's argument that all language and all communication are forms of translation. The map which Lancey and Yolland are making, for example, is a translation of landscape on to paper. The book which Hugh tells Yolland he is writing is a translation of school lessons into a textbook. There are other examples of translation as interpretation or misrepresentation.

When Owen translates Lancey's announcements in Act I, he changes the meanings of what Lancey says, and makes them less suspect to the people of Baile Beag. Yolland calls Owen 'Roland' (p. 54) which is an interesting translation of 'Owen', which Yolland either misheard or could not pronounce properly, into a sound which is very like 'Yolland'.

This suggests that translation is always an act of making something which is strange sound more familiar and comfortable to us. The theme of baptism, which translates a person or thing into a named identity, appears several times in the play also. Steiner argued that language exists to communicate and to conceal, and that distinct languages were formed out of the need for privacy. Language could be used, therefore, to define a tribe or people by a common set of codes for communication, but it could also be used to exclude those who did not belong to the tribe. The conversion of a people from one language to another, as it takes place in Friel's play, suggests that the people are being integrated with another tribe so that they can have no privacies or intimacies of their own.

Many Irish writers have dealt with the problems of speaking English. As far back as Joyce's *A Portrait of the Artist as a Young Man*, Stephen Dedalus had a feeling that the English language would never fully belong to Irish people: 'The language in which we are speaking is his before it is mine... His language, so familiar and so foreign, will always be for me an acquired speech. I have not made or accepted its words. My voice holds them at bay. My soul frets in the shadow of his language' (Joyce, 1992: 146). Friel himself has commented on the relationship between the warring communities in the North of Ireland as a problem of language (see below).

The transcendental nature of translation is alluded to by Yolland and Owen in Act II scene 1, as they become increasingly drunk on poteen, and on their own creative power: 'We name a thing and – bang! It leaps into existence!' (p. 56). They compare their power to assign names to things and beings with that of God in the Garden of Eden, as told in Genesis. It is also an allusion to modern language theories, such as those of Ferdinand de Saussure, who taught that

CHECK THE BOOK
Chapter Five of James Joyce's *A Portrait of the Artist as a Young Man* contains a scene in which Stephen discusses words with the Dean of Studies in University College Dublin, and an Englishman. As he does so, he becomes aware that the language will never entirely be his, even though it is the language he speaks from birth.

language was merely a shared convention, without any connection to the things it names, so that it differentiates rather than names. Wittgenstein maintained that language was a matter of custom and practice, merely a 'game' with shared rules. Yolland has just decided to keep the original form of Tobair Vree and Owen has insisted on the genuine form of his name, so their gleeful celebration of the power of inventing new names is **ironic**. But when Manus enters he has no knowledge of this context, and their laughter and boasting about changing the names must seem to him obscene and sinister.

FAILURE OF COMMUNICATION

In many ways, *Translations* is a pessimistic play, particularly about the capacity of people from different cultures to communicate to each other. There are clearly several major differences between the Irish and English characters in the language they speak, the values they cherish and the cultural beliefs they hold. It is possible for them to resolve their differences, or at least to ignore their differences, by celebrating what they love about each other's culture, as Maire and Yolland do. But both sides fail to express themselves, or their real feelings, to each other, and they resort instead to violence and destruction, as we know is particularly the case with Lancey and the Donnelly twins. This situation, of violence as a sign of the failure to communicate in language, obviously has resonances for the situation in Northern Ireland in 1980, when the possibility of peaceful discussions between the Irish nationalists, the Northern unionists and the British and Irish governments seemed to be very far away.

There are several other examples in the play of the failure of communication more generally. Yolland fails to understand what several characters say to him. Owen doesn't communicate his feelings fully to Yolland. Manus doesn't express his feelings fully to Maire. Manus makes 'the wrong gesture in the wrong language' (p. 55). The play is rife with such incidents in which characters fail to make themselves understood, and fail to understand what is being said to them. *Translations* is highlighting the importance of language, and communication in general, for the conflicts between different groups of people.

CHECK THE BOOK

In Friel's play *Wonderful Tennessee*, the character George rarely speaks, he has throat cancer and it causes pain to do so. Instead, he plays the accordion, and the music serves as a form of wordless communication, which reflects and provides incidental music to the main themes of the play – uncertainty, communication and alienation from the modern world. In a way, George performs the same function as Sarah in *Translations*, but the function has been expanded greatly.

Friel argued that language was particularly significant in Northern Ireland: 'I think that is how the political problem of this island is going to be solved. It's going to be solved by the recognition of what language means for us on this island. Because we are in fact talking about accommodation or marrying of two cultures here, which are ostensibly speaking the same language but which in fact aren't' (Delaney, *Brian Friel in Conversation*, 2000, pp. 176–7). The idea that two groups of people can be 'ostensibly speaking the same language' while in fact speaking two very different languages is a key to understanding why Friel has presented both communities (Irish and English) speaking through the medium of English. It allows him to show his audience that the two sets of characters are saying very different things.

IRELAND: ISLAND OF SAINTS AND SCHOLARS?

There is a popular view, to some extent endorsed by politicians, that Ireland, before the advent of the British, was a world of prelapsarian contentment, filled with saintly scholars and scholarly saints. Many critics have taken the view that Friel intended Baile Beag to be seen in this way – as a contented and self-contained civilisation destroyed by outside contamination. Friel is often accused of being (or praised as being, depending on one's own cultural affiliations) a playwright who sees contentment and spirituality in the Irish countryside. The critic Elmer Andrews (writing of *Wonderful Tennessee*) speaks of rural Ireland's 'powers to compel and perhaps even to renew' (Elmer Andrews, *The Art of Brian Friel: Neither Dream nor Reality*, 1995, p. 260). Friel himself is obviously troubled by these assertions. In relation to Gaelic Ireland, he has remarked: 'I have no nostalgia for that time. I think one should look back on the process of history with some kind of coolness...people commented that the opening scenes of the play were a portrait of some kind of idyllic, Forest of Arden life. But this is a complete illusion...' (Delaney, *Brian Friel in Conversation*, 2000, p. 148). It is, in fact, very dangerous to interpret Friel in this way, as his use of the Irish landscape is, at best, ambiguous. In *The Gentle Island*, two hikers stay with a community on one of the islands off the coast, only to be caught in an eruption of homoerotic violence.

CONTEXT

It is unclear to what extent the outburst in *The Gentle Island* was provoked or catalysed by the presence of the strangers. Friel, as one would expect, leaves us with no answers.

In *The Communication Cord*, 1983, Friel debunks the notion of saintly peasants in the person of Nora Dan (whose name is also used in *Translations*): 'The quintessential noble peasant – obsessed with curiosity and greed and envy' (p. 21). Neither are the Irish characters in *Translations* without a plethora of problems: Hugh is an alcoholic, Manus is crippled, Sarah is 'dumb', Jimmy is filthy and lost in his own little world, and Doalty is thick. Innocence, certainly in sexual terms, is not a feature of the play. Nellie Ruadh has had a child out of wedlock, or at least by a man not her husband, and the baby subsequently dies.

There are not many saints in *Translations*, but the play does explore the myth that Ireland was a land of great learning and scholarship. There has been debate about the accuracy of the play in suggesting that the hedge-schools of Ireland were havens of classical scholars, with some historians disputing the suggestion that the hedge-schools taught anything more than elementary skills of arithmetic, writing and reading. Most of the pupils in Hugh's hedge-school appear, however successfully, to be in the process of learning Greek or Latin, and Hugh, Manus and Jimmy Jack obviously have a command of several languages. Hugh, for example, knows four languages, writes poetry in Latin, and purports to be writing textbooks for instructing students in five languages. The classical learning of the local people seems to be embedded in Jimmy and Hugh's way of life. Jimmy quotes Virgil's advice on agriculture, for example, and both he and Hugh make constant parallels between the English colonisation of Ireland and the Roman imperial conquests. Hugh contends that Gaelic language and literature are rooted in the classical learning of Europe, whereas he treats English literature as a minor provincial genre. Where Friel complicates the myth is in the suggestion that the learning is useless, a knowledge of Greek is of little use to Hugh in acquiring the principalship of the new National School. Instead the job goes, ironically, to a man skilled in 'bacon-curing' (p. 85). For all the comparisons between the Roman empire and the British one, Hugh appears to approve of Roman imperialist culture while scorning its modern counterpart. Likewise his determined ignorance of Wordsworth betrays the deep prejudice at the heart of his scholarship.

CHECK THE BOOK

It is worth looking at Reg Hindley, *The Death of the Irish Language*, 1990, which examines the causes of its decline from the eighteenth century onwards.

The world of Baile Beag is also deeply tribal. At the end of the play, Jimmy Jack muses on the meanings of *endogamein* and *exogamein*, meaning to marry within and without the tribe (p. 90). Marrying outside the tribe was bound to cause trouble in both 'tribes'. Ostensibly, Jimmy is commenting, not on the relationship between Maire and Yolland, but on the relationship between the goddess Athene and himself. Friel, however, is speaking both of the difficulty with the relationship between Maire and Yolland, that it crossed tribal barriers, and of the situation in Northern Ireland, where the two tribes remain at odds. There is a hint here that Yolland has been harmed in some way because he crossed those barriers.

CHECK THE BOOK
The tribalism in Friel's work is dealt with in Tony Corbett, *Brian Friel: Decoding the Language of the Tribe*, 2002.

ENGLISH UPSTARTS

Hugh in particular presents Gaelic culture as an ancient set of honourable traditions and customs which are dignified and civilised, and he contrasts it with English culture, which he thinks is base and materialistic. The Gaelic chieftains, from one family of whom – the O'Donnell chieftains – Hugh is descended, often viewed the English invaders and colonisers as upstarts who had no noble blood in their veins and no culture of learning or civilisation. Hugh's criticism of the English language, that it is particularly suited to commerce, is characteristic of the attitude which the Gaelic nobles expressed about the English in the sixteenth and seventeenth centuries. The English colonisers in Ireland seemed to be more interested in the pursuit of money and power than in nobler spiritual and intellectual endeavours. Of course, Hugh's criticisms of the English are **ironic**, because he has material and commercial needs as much as any Englishman, and it is easy to claim spiritual superiority, especially when one is materially bereft. Lancey and Yolland are depicted as having no classical learning, and so they are made to appear rather weak intellectually, but this is hardly likely to have been the case for English military officers at this time. There are, therefore, a few myths purveyed in the play about the differences between the noble Irish and the base English.

In a later play, *Making History* (1989), Friel looks more closely at the noble Irish in the persons of Hugh O'Neill and Red Hugh O'Donnell, two of the most significant sixteenth- and seventeenth-

CONTEXT

In *Making History*,
1989, Friel uses
another 'theatrical
conceit' to convey
Hugh O'Neill's
divided nature. In
the stage
directions to Act I
of *Making History*,
he tells us that
O'Neill speaks
with a cultured
English accent,
which, in moments
of emotion
becomes 'pure
Tyrone' (the
Northern Irish
county of which
O'Neill is earl).

century leaders. O'Neill is presented as a deeply divided
Renaissance leader, motivated by pragmatism, and O'Donnell as a
local chieftain with only the vaguest idea of the bigger historical
picture. They are no more and no less noble than the English who
surround them.

DRAMATIC TECHNIQUES

STRUCTURE

The play's story is tightly constructed. It begins by introducing the
audience to the situation. A village community in Ireland, whose
eccentric characters gather in the hedge-school, is to be mapped and
its place names anglicised and standardised for the map. English
soldiers are to carry out this task. Act I defines the characters and
explores some of the relationships between them, including the
relationship between Owen and Manus, between Hugh and Jimmy
Jack, and between Manus and Maire. The situation is then
complicated as some of the implications of this project become
more apparent. The standardising of the place names will mean that
the linguistic and cultural traditions of the Irish community will be
compromised and even destroyed. The mapping and renaming
exercise now begins to appear threatening. One of the English
soldiers, Yolland, is unhappy with the project, and he comes to love
the community, and particularly one of its inhabitants, Maire. There
are also strong tensions between the characters which will be
exposed further in the final Act. Manus is clearly jealous of the
relationship between Yolland and Maire. Hugh is already hinting
that the world around him is about to be transformed, and suggests
that this doesn't really surprise him. These complications now move
swiftly towards a tense and tragic conclusion. Yolland goes missing,
feared killed by local rebels. The army reacts violently to his
disappearance and begins to destroy crops, fences and livestock. The
rebels respond with more violence, and an air of uncertainty and
fear hangs over the villagers. At the conclusion of the play their
whole way of life looks as if it may be coming to an end.

The structure of *Translations* allows Friel to explore several layers
of events and themes. On one level, it is about a series of local

incidents in a small village in northwest Ireland in 1833, which compel the characters to change the ways in which they live. On another level, it is about the theme of cross-cultural conflict and communication, about whether or not any two groups of people, anywhere in the world, can exist together harmoniously, especially when one group is dominated by the other. The play can be read or performed for its political messages, its human concerns, its dramatic qualities, its historical interests, its linguistic concerns, or, indeed for all these matters. In a simple setting, with a relatively small cast of characters, *Translations* has managed to represent a wide continuum of themes and interests.

THE DONNELLY TWINS

Plays frequently use characters who do not appear, but who are referred to frequently for dramatic effect. Moton's play *Speed the Plough* (1789) had the famous line 'What will Mrs Grundy say?' Although Mrs Grundy never appeared, her dampening moral presence was felt by the other characters. Similarly, the Donnelly twins never appear, but their presence, or rather their absence, becomes darker as the play progresses. The first reference is in Act I, during the roll-call, Manus asks if they are coming to class any more. This would not have been an unusual question in a school where attendance was casual and self-motivated. Their absence suggests that they are engaged in mischief, particularly from the manner in which Doalty seems to be evasive about them, hinting that he knows more than he has revealed. Bridget then informs Manus that two of the soldiers' horses were found at the bottom of a cliff, casting suspicion on the Donnelly twins. It becomes apparent that the Donnelly twins are behind most of the aggression in the play, a dark and violent underside to the Gaelic idyll.

In Act II scene 1, Yolland casually asks Owen if he knows the twins. This indicates that they have now come to the attention of the authorities. Owen is dismissive, adding the information that they were fishermen, but he was not aware of the conversation in Act I. The detail about their proficiency as fishermen is to show that they are people with a standing to protect, not merely n'er-do-well troublemakers. By Act III, Bridget, referring to Yolland's disappearance, can state: 'If you want to know about Yolland, ask

> **CONTEXT**
>
> Friel has been accused of having fundamentalist republican leanings in the way in which he deals with some characters. *The Freedom of the City* and *Volunteers*, in particular, attracted this kind of (unjustified) criticism. By leaving the Donnelly twins offstage, he avoids the possibility of having to look on them sympathetically or otherwise.

the Donnelly twins' (p. 75). By the end of the act, the Donnelly twins have moved from pranksters like Doalty, to full-blown guerrilla-style terrorists. 'The Donnelly twins know how' (p. 84), says Doalty, meaning that they know how to resist the army. Their use of guerrilla war tactics means that they can strike at the army fast and when they least expect it, and then disappear so that they don't get caught. What Doalty doesn't see is that the Donnelly twins have also deserted the people of Baile Beag, and left them to suffer the violent backlash from the army. Doalty has also moved from just 'slightly thick', to someone who is about to join the rebels. Ordinary people are being corrupted by circumstances, and are choosing violence as a means of resolution. Friel, by not making a moral judgement on the characters, leaves the audience to approve or disapprove, depending on their own allegiances.

LANGUAGE AND TRANSLATION

Translations presents two groups of people with different languages. The English soldiers arrive without any knowledge of Gaelic, and most of the Irish inhabitants of Baile Beag do not have any knowledge of English. Friel is interested in exploring the difficulties of how these two groups of people communicate with one another, but the problem is that not many of his audiences will have knowledge of Gaelic. Both Irish and English characters are therefore represented through the English language. The audiences are informed early in the play that they are to believe that the Irish characters are speaking in Gaelic:

> MAIRE: That's the height of my Latin. Fit me better if I had even that much English.
>
> JIMMY: English? I thought you had some English?
>
> MAIRE: Three words. (p. 8)

Friel uses a number of ways of reminding his audiences that Gaelic is being spoken. The Irish characters sometimes talk about not knowing any English. The English characters sometimes show that they are unable to understand what is being spoken by the Irish characters. The Irish characters are also differentiated from the English ones in their speech patterns, with **Hiberno-English**

CONTEXT

The TV comedy series *'Allo 'Allo!* used a similar technique to Friel's. When characters were speaking English, they spoke with English accents, when they were speaking French, they spoke with French accents, and similarly with Germans. Variations on pronunciation and syntax allowed the writers to exploit the technique for comic purposes. A comparison with Friel's 'theatrical conceit' is useful and amusing.

Friel argued that language was particularly significant in Northern
Ireland: 'I think that is how the political problem of this island is
going to be solved. It's going to be solved by the recognition of
what language means for us on this island. Because we are in fact
talking about accommodation or marrying of two cultures here,
which are ostensibly speaking the same language but which in fact
aren't' (Delaney, *Brian Friel in Conversation*, 2000, pp. 176–7). The
idea that two groups of people can be 'ostensibly speaking the same
language' while in fact speaking two very different languages is a
key to understanding why Friel has presented both communities
(Irish and English) speaking through the medium of English. It
allows him to show his audience that the two sets of characters are
saying very different things.

IRELAND: ISLAND OF SAINTS AND SCHOLARS?

There is a popular view, to some extent endorsed by politicians, that
Ireland, before the advent of the British, was a world of prelapsarian
contentment, filled with saintly scholars and scholarly saints. Many
critics have taken the view that Friel intended Baile Beag to be seen
in this way – as a contented and self-contained civilisation destroyed
by outside contamination. Friel is often accused of being (or praised
as being, depending on one's own cultural affiliations) a playwright
who sees contentment and spirituality in the Irish countryside. The
critic Elmer Andrews (writing of *Wonderful Tennessee*) speaks of
rural Ireland's 'powers to compel and perhaps even to renew'
(Elmer Andrews, *The Art of Brian Friel: Neither Dream nor
Reality*, 1995, p. 260). Friel himself is obviously troubled by these
assertions. In relation to Gaelic Ireland, he has remarked: 'I have no
nostalgia for that time. I think one should look back on the process
of history with some kind of coolness...people commented that the
opening scenes of the play were a portrait of some kind of idyllic,
Forest of Arden life. But this is a complete illusion...' (Delaney,
Brian Friel in Conversation, 2000, p. 148). It is, in fact, very
dangerous to interpret Friel in this way, as his use of the Irish
landscape is, at best, ambiguous. In *The Gentle Island*, two hikers
stay with a community on one of the islands off the coast, only to
be caught in an eruption of homoerotic violence.

CONTEXT

It is unclear to
what extent the
outburst in *The
Gentle Island* was
provoked or
catalysed by the
presence of the
strangers. Friel, as
one would expect,
leaves us with no
answers.

In *The Communication Cord*, 1983, Friel debunks the notion of saintly peasants in the person of Nora Dan (whose name is also used in *Translations*): 'The quintessential noble peasant – obsessed with curiosity and greed and envy' (p. 21). Neither are the Irish characters in *Translations* without a plethora of problems: Hugh is an alcoholic, Manus is crippled, Sarah is 'dumb', Jimmy is filthy and lost in his own little world, and Doalty is thick. Innocence, certainly in sexual terms, is not a feature of the play. Nellie Ruadh has had a child out of wedlock, or at least by a man not her husband, and the baby subsequently dies.

There are not many saints in *Translations*, but the play does explore the myth that Ireland was a land of great learning and scholarship. There has been debate about the accuracy of the play in suggesting that the hedge-schools of Ireland were havens of classical scholars, with some historians disputing the suggestion that the hedge-schools taught anything more than elementary skills of arithmetic, writing and reading. Most of the pupils in Hugh's hedge-school appear, however successfully, to be in the process of learning Greek or Latin, and Hugh, Manus and Jimmy Jack obviously have a command of several languages. Hugh, for example, knows four languages, writes poetry in Latin, and purports to be writing textbooks for instructing students in five languages. The classical learning of the local people seems to be embedded in Jimmy and Hugh's way of life. Jimmy quotes Virgil's advice on agriculture, for example, and both he and Hugh make constant parallels between the English colonisation of Ireland and the Roman imperial conquests. Hugh contends that Gaelic language and literature are rooted in the classical learning of Europe, whereas he treats English literature as a minor provincial genre. Where Friel complicates the myth is in the suggestion that the learning is useless, a knowledge of Greek is of little use to Hugh in acquiring the principalship of the new National School. Instead the job goes, ironically, to a man skilled in 'bacon-curing' (p. 85). For all the comparisons between the Roman empire and the British one, Hugh appears to approve of Roman imperialist culture while scorning its modern counterpart. Likewise his determined ignorance of Wordsworth betrays the deep prejudice at the heart of his scholarship.

CHECK THE BOOK

It is worth looking at Reg Hindley, *The Death of the Irish Language*, 1990, which examines the causes of its decline from the eighteenth century onwards.

grammar, for example, and in their dress and names. This device of presenting two languages through the medium of one is a crucial component of the play since it enables Friel to present us with two communities who are alienated from each other by a language barrier, without alienating the audiences from the play by that same language barrier, and it reflects the fact that most Irish audiences today do not speak Gaelic.

THE ENDING

One of the most conventional structures for a play is to begin with a situation, then introduce some complications, before moving towards a resolution. As outlined in the section on 'Structure' above, Friel's *Translations* follows this convention in the first two Acts, but in Act III he avoids resolving the situation. Yolland is missing, and we do not find out what has happened to him. Maire wants to leave, but we do not know if she will ever emigrate. Manus has left, and we do not know if the soldiers will suspect him of complicity in Yolland's disappearance. Hugh ends the play in confusion, unable to remember a passage from Virgil which he once used to know. There appear to be many 'loose ends' in the play, lots of uncertainties which are unresolved. The play ends at the very point at which the community which we have been watching or reading about may be destroyed by the army, but we do not find out what happens to it. We might think that this is a weakness in the play. But there might be reasons for these loose ends. Given what we know about the Donnelly twins, and what they represent historically, it is most likely that Yolland has been killed. Given what we know about emigration around this time, it is likely that Maire did emigrate. And given what we know about English army actions in Ireland, it is likely that the community was damaged in some way, and some people may even have been killed. The play might be depending on our impressions or knowledge of Irish history to fill in some of the blanks. Hugh's confusion is quite appropriate at the conclusion to the play, as Hugh has told Jimmy just a few minutes beforehand that 'confusion is not an ignoble condition' (p. 67). If we are confused at the end of the play, then, it may be because Friel is attempting to convey to his audience the uncertainty and confusion which were the result for Irish people of the events depicted in the play, and leaving the audience free to

CHECK THE BOOK

Marilynn J. Richtarik's *Acting Between the Lines*, 1994, is a detailed study of the Field Day Company, which Brian Friel founded in order to perform *Translations* in Derry.

make their own judgements about those events. Real life avoids neat endings.

LANGUAGE AND STYLE

CLASS AND EDUCATION

There are differences between the language used by the characters in *Translations* which can be attributed to their social class or level of education. Hugh and Lancey, for example, are both highly articulate in their speech, and have more in common in the way they speak than Hugh and Doalty. Some productions have made a feature out of this. The 1996 revival of *Translations* at the Abbey Theatre in Dublin had Hugh speaking in an English accent. As a more anglicised accent has often been taken as a sign of higher social class in Ireland, this conveyed the sense that Hugh differed from most of his pupils in terms of class identity. Manus and Owen also differ in their speech, with Manus speaking in more local tones, using **colloquialisms,** for example, whereas Owen, coming from his life as '*a city man*' (p. 26) in Dublin, adopts a pompous (even if **ironic**) tone: 'My job is to translate the quaint, archaic tongue you people persist in speaking into the King's good English' (p. 29). Even the fact that Hugh, Manus and Owen know the English language marks them out as being of a higher class than Doalty, Maire and Bridget.

GEORGE STEINER

Friel was inspired by many of George Steiner's arguments in *After Babel*, 1975, about language and translation. Steiner argued, for instance, that when languages disappeared, the identities of the communities which used them tended to dissolve too. With the death of a language, a whole way of thinking, living and acting died too: 'Each takes with it a storehouse of consciousness' (Steiner, 1975, p. 54). Friel was evidently moved by the implication that with the decline of the Gaelic language in the nineteenth century went a whole chunk of Irish culture and society. Steiner also argued that languages died out not because of any inherent weakness in the language, but because the language was not in touch with the 'principal currents of intellectual and political force. Countless

CONTEXT

When Hugh declares in Act III: 'To remember everything is a form of madness' (p. 88), Friel is putting the words of George Steiner into his mouth. The complete quote in *After Babel,* 1975, is: 'To remember everything is a condition of madness. We remember culturally, as we do individually, by conventions of emphasis, foreshortening, and omission' (p. 29). What this means is that the actual events of the past are less important than the perception of those events.

tribal societies have withered inward, isolated by language barriers even from their near neighbours' (p. 56). The fact that Hugh claims never to have heard of Wordsworth may be a sign that his language and culture have failed to keep up with the modern world, even the major events and trends of their nearest neighbour. Their only source of inspiration appears to be ancient Greek and Latin, which means that they have no contact with other living cultures and languages. Steiner's book had a lot to say about the untranslatability of one language to another. Something always gets lost in translation, because there is no absolute equivalence between languages. It is, therefore, impossible to escape from misunderstanding and confusion in the translation of one language into another, and Steiner made it clear that translation occurred within languages as much as between languages. We translate complex words into simple ones, unfamiliar phrases into familiar ones, and in the process we cannot avoid changing the meaning of words and phrases, however slightly. Steiner argued therefore that 'true understanding is possible only when there is silence' (p. 286), which is the only 'language' which cannot be mistranslated. Sarah is obviously an important reminder of this argument in *Translations*.

CHECK THE BOOK

'Any model of communication is at the same time a model of translation, of a vertical or horizontal transfer of significance. No two historical epochs, no two social classes, no two localities, use words and syntax to signify exactly the same things ... Neither do two human beings', George Steiner, 1975, p. 46.

PART FOUR

CRITICAL HISTORY

REVIEWS AND CONTROVERSIES

The first performance of Friel's *Translations* took place on 23 September 1980 in the Guildhall, Derry. It was directed by Art O'Briain and was presented by the Field Day Theatre Company. It was an instant success, with the opening productions sold out, and it has been almost in constant production in Ireland and elsewhere ever since. It was interpreted first as an attempt to represent early nineteenth-century Ireland accurately on stage, despite the fact that Friel did not intend it to be seen principally as an historical play.

CONTEXT

The fact that the critics were unable to agree on a single theme for the play is evidence of its complex and multi-layered nature. It took some time for *Translations* to be seen as a play about the nature and importance of language.

The reviews were generally favourable, but they indicated considerable differences in how the play was interpreted. Colm Cronin of *The Sunday Tribune*, for example, saw the play as a treatise 'on the failure of a people to cherish and preserve the riches of their culture', whereas Fintan O'Toole in *Ireland and the Arts* interpreted the play as being about 'the historical disjunction caused by the forced shift of Irish speech from the Gaelic language to English'. Cronin thought the play was blaming the Irish for losing their language, while O'Toole saw it as blaming the English for destroying Gaelic.

Some critics believed that the play was sanctioning violence, and others believed that it was condemning violence. Martha McClelland, writing for *An Phoblacht*, the newspaper of the IRA, argued that the play was celebrating as heroic Doalty's decision to organise violent resistance to the army: 'It is Doalty who knows how to deal with the present and defend culture most effectively.' Martin Esslin, on the other hand, writing in *Plays and Players*, suggested that the play was highlighting 'the moral dilemma of those in Ireland who desire independence and national freedom but abhor violence in any form'. For Esslin, the play was not celebrating violence, but depicting as tragic the situation in which people felt compelled to fight.

There were also a number of controversies concerning the historical accuracy of the play. The Irish historian Sean Connolly described the play as 'a distortion of the real nature and causes of cultural change in nineteenth-century Ireland so extreme as to go beyond mere factual error'. Particularly controversial were the final scenes in which characters reported seeing the engineers destroying fences, trampling crops and rifling through the countryside with bayonets. J. H. Andrews, who otherwise thought the play was a subtle blend of historical truths, argued in an essay in *The Irish Review* that Friel had represented the engineers inaccurately. The engineers were not permitted to carry out evictions or threats of any kind, and were not armed when they conducted the ordnance survey. Most of the staff of the ordnance survey project were not even English soldiers but Irish civilians. And most of the place names were not invented by the engineers but had already been anglicised for years, and sometimes centuries, before. Friel's play was criticised for distorting the past and inventing a purely fictitious nationalist version of history.

He in turn refuted the suggestion that the play was supposed to be historically accurate at all, and in the programme to *Making History* in 1988 he stated clearly from the outset that 'when there was a tension between historical "fact" and the imperative of fiction, I'm glad to say I kept faith with the narrative'. It is possible to read *Making History*, which features an historian who distorts the facts deliberately for the purpose of inventing a national hero, as a response to the critics who argued that *Translations* was a distortion of history, just as *The Communication Cord*, 1983, can be read as a response to those critics who argued that *Translations* presented a naïve rural idyll.

Despite these controversies, Friel's *Translations* has become a national classic of Irish drama, and has become renowned worldwide, according to Fintan O'Toole, 'as a definitive statement about the nature and meaning of colonialism'. Friel may have distorted the historical facts, but he has created a masterful piece of dramatic writing which is capable in performance of making the tragedy of the conflict between Ireland and England moving and poignant. O'Toole argued in *The Irish Times* in 1996, on the

> **CONTEXT**
>
> Friel was criticised for being 'nationalist', a polite way of saying anti-British. The portrait of Lancey may make this seem so, if taken in isolation. But Friel's portrait of Hugh is no less cruel in its inception. Jimmy Jack is as laughable throughout as Lancey is in Act I. Granted, the soldiers carrying out the survey did not evict anyone, but their counterparts in other regiments certainly did. Friel is employing an artistic 'shorthand' to write a play, not a work of history.

CONTEXT

The Abbey Theatre, which considered itself the custodian of Irish tradition and of the Irish psyche, at least insofar as it related to drama, was responsible for much of the peasant drama that emerged in the 'First Wave' of Irish playwriting.

occasion of the play being revived at the Abbey Theatre, that the play was 'all too accurate about the present', and that it contained an 'underlying feeling for the tragedy of people who get caught up in myths and mindsets that cannot adapt to change'. At a time when the possibilities for peace in Northern Ireland were looking gloomy as a ceasefire was wrecked by people whose mindsets were slow to change, O'Toole argued that the greatest achievement of the play was not its representation of nineteenth-century Ireland but its message to late twentieth-century Ireland that ambiguous and confused identities were worth the price if peace was the result.

PART FIVE

BACKGROUND

BRIAN FRIEL'S LIFE AND WORK

Brian Friel was born in Omagh, County Tyrone in Northern Ireland on 5 January, 1929. His father was a teacher from Derry city, and his mother was from a Gaelic-speaking area of County Donegal. When he was ten years old he moved with his family to Derry, where he attended St Columb's College, a Catholic boys school. He then went to the Irish Republic to study for the priesthood in St Patrick's College, Maynooth, but left three years later to begin a teacher's training course in St Joseph's College, Belfast. He worked as a teacher in Derry throughout the 1950s, during which time he began to write short stories. He married, in 1954, Anne Morrison, with whom he would have five children. By 1955 he was publishing stories in American magazines, and three years later he wrote several radio plays which were performed on BBC radio.

In 1960 Friel left the teaching profession and became a full-time writer. His reputation as a playwright grew throughout the 1960s. His first stage play, *The Enemy Within*, was produced at the Abbey Theatre in Dublin. His knowledge and understanding of stage techniques, however, were greatly enhanced by a visit to fellow Ulsterman, Tyrone Guthrie, in Minneapolis, USA, where Guthrie ran a theatre company. Friel continued to publish short stories at the same time as his plays were becoming increasingly renowned.

He moved over the border to the Irish Republic in 1967, to Muff first, and, after 1982, to Greencastle, both in Donegal. He was troubled deeply by the outbreak of sectarian and political conflict in Northern Ireland in 1969, and he responded in his plays to the historical and political issues raised in this conflict. In 1980 Friel teamed up with the actor Stephen Rea to produce Friel's new play, *Translations*, but could only get funding from the Northern Ireland Arts Council for a theatre company rather than a play. They decided, therefore, to found a theatre company which they called

CONTEXT

Friel's collections of short stories, *A Saucer of Larks* and *The Gold in the Sea*, often illuminate the later plays. *Dancing at Lughnasa* was very similar to 'A Man's World', while parts of *Aristocrats* are based on 'Foundry House'. Friel's earlier craft of story writer often emerges in the detailed and significant stage directions and notes that he writes to his plays.

'Field Day'. The Field Day Theatre Company has proved to be one of the most important developments in contemporary Irish theatre. It was based in Derry city and brought world theatrical premieres to this city, before touring in London, New York and the provincial towns of Ireland. It attempted to draw on the Catholic and Protestant traditions of Northern Ireland in an effort to bring the two communities closer together.

CHECK THE BOOK

Anthony Roche, *Contemporary Irish Drama*, 1994, contains chapters on Brian Friel's plays.

Friel wrote some of his most innovative plays, *Translations* and *Making History*, in the 1980s, and had them produced by Field Day. He later resigned from Field Day, in 1994, on the grounds that he believed artistic integrity was being compromised by the political arguments which were surrounding the company. He has been acknowledged for his tremendous achievements in drama and literature, however. The Republic of Ireland appointed him as a senator in the Irish Senate, the upper house of government, in 1987. In 1989 he was honoured by the BBC for his achievements in modern drama when they put on a six-play season of his plays, the first time the BBC has honoured a living playwright in this way.

HIS WRITINGS

Friel's writing career can be divided roughly into three phases. In the first phase, from 1952 to 1964, he wrote short stories, radio plays and stage plays which were chiefly preoccupied with the private individual, and with the effects of childhood experiences on adult life, but there are also hints of later concerns with communication difficulties and with Irishness. His publishing career began in 1955 when he published two stories in *The New Yorker*. He then had two radio plays performed on BBC Northern Ireland Radio and BBC Radio – *A Sort of Freedom* and *To This Hard House*. His first stage play to be produced was *The Enemy Within*, a play about St Columba's dilemma in Iona between his religious calling and the demands of his family and home in Ireland. It was performed first at the Abbey Theatre in Dublin in 1962.

In the second phase of his career, from 1964 to 1988, Friel concentrated mostly on plays, which showed a growing interest in exploring the impact of national and global historical forces on the lives of private individuals and local communities, reaching what are generally regarded to be his greatest achievements in *Translations* in 1980 and *Making History* in 1988. During this period he was exploring controversial subjects – Irish emigration (*Philadelphia, Here I Come*, 1964), the political independence of the Republic of Ireland (*The Mundy Scheme*, 1969, a play he later withdrew from the public domain), the shooting of civilians in Derry city (*The Freedom of the City*, 1973), the destruction of Gaelic language and culture (*Translations*, 1980) and the clash of Irish and English military forces and cultural imperatives in the late sixteenth century (*Making History*, 1988). He also interrogated the idea of Irish peasant life as a form of perfection in *The Gentle Island* (1971), which deals with themes of violence and homosexuality. Another play, now acknowledged as a masterpiece, *Faith Healer*, opened New York in 1979, and closed after nine performances. It deals with the relationship between language and reality in the conflicting monologues of its three characters.

The Communication Cord followed directly on *Translations*, and is seen, even by Friel, as a companion piece. It is a farce, set in a modernised cow-byre, now used as a weekend retreat by urbanites. It sets past against present, urban against rural and Gaelic against foreigner and explores many of the themes of *Translations*, but to comic effect.

After 1988, in the third phase of his career, he turned away from writing plays as national **epics** or **historical dramas**, and seemed to concentrate on earlier personal and autobiographical themes. *Dancing at Lughnasa* (1990), *Molly Sweeney* (1994) and *Give Me Your Answer, Do!* (1997) all address concerns with the individual psyche and personal liberation more closely than was evident throughout the 1960s, 1970s and 1980s. There are two ways of seeing this return in his later career to personal themes. The first is that he is retreating from the controversial historical and political issues for which he became famous and was heavily criticised. The second is that he felt that he had written everything he wanted to say about larger historical and political themes after he finished *Making History* in 1988, and has since moved on.

CHECK THE BOOK

The Communication Cord, 1983, sheds a great deal of light on *Translations*. Friel has said that the earlier play was such a success and attracted many critical and popular opinions that he never intended for it. *The Communication Cord* is the antidote to the seriousness with which the theatre-going public received *Translations*.

HISTORICAL BACKGROUND

In 1833, the year in which *Translations* is set, Ireland remained a predominantly rural, Catholic, Gaelic-speaking country. It was under English colonial rule, as a result of a series of invasions and plantations which took place between 1169 and 1603, and had been annexed to Britain in the 1801 Act of Union. Under colonial rule, the Irish people suffered a number of disadvantages. They were punished for belonging to Catholic or Dissenter religions when England was an Anglican-Protestant country. They were forbidden to practise non-Anglican faiths or to receive an education. They were also barred from owning land of any substantial amount and from entering professional occupations. These 'penal laws' were enforced throughout the country until the end of the eighteenth century, and they were not removed fully until 1829 with the Catholic Emancipation Act. By that time, the laws had caused considerable damage to Irish society and culture. Catholics were allowed to become traders and merchants, for example, but to do so they invariably had to learn the English language. So too, Catholics could become landowners if they converted to the Anglican faith. There was always a cost involved for an individual to advance up the social and economic ladder. By the beginning of the nineteenth century, this had created a situation in which the middle and upper classes in Ireland spoke English, were predominantly Anglican-Protestant, and either owned land or worked in professional occupations in the towns, while the lower classes in Ireland spoke Gaelic, were predominantly Catholic, and were tenants on the land with smallholdings and no legal protection from unfair rents or eviction.

This division in Irish society resulted in disaffection and resentment among the lower classes. Many chose to emigrate to the United States, where they believed they could start a new better life, without fear of discrimination or poverty. Others chose to rebel against British rule, by taking up arms against the colonial army. The play reflects these responses in a number of ways: Maire chooses to emigrate; Hugh and Jimmy Jack were inspired to take up arms against Britain in the 1798 Rebellion, although they didn't get

www. CHECK THE NET
For a collection of digital images and transcriptions which relate to the Act of Union, 1801, visit **http://link.bubl.ac. uk/historyireland**.

very far; and the Donnelly twins are believed to be organising their own campaigns of local violent resistance against the English soldiers in Baile Beag. Irish Catholics and Dissenters had also found ways of evading the penal laws. Local communities gathered together to practise their faiths in open-air rock masses or barn services in remote places, where the authorities would not find them, and they had also formed hedge-schools, so called because they were at first held in hedgerows. Later they moved into more stable lodgings, such as the cow-shed Hugh uses in the play.

In the early nineteenth century, the population of Ireland grew rapidly, to a peak of over 8 million people in 1841. The land was divided and subdivided between the sons of farmers who already lived on smallholdings, until many of the farms, particularly in the west of Ireland, were unable to sustain even the most meagre existence. The Irish people turned to the potato crop as the staple ingredient in their diet. It would grow in abundance, with little attention, and it contained most of the nourishment they needed. They became dependent on the potato crop, but it was struck by blight and disease fourteen times between 1816 and 1842, including the year 1833. A fungus attacked the potato plant in damp and muggy conditions, the leaves withered and turned black, and the potatoes decomposed and emitted a sweet stench of decay. This is what Bridget smells several times in the play. Potato crops were devastated, and the failure of the British government to provide adequate relief measures, which caused the Great Famine of 1845 to 1850, during which 1 million people died and 1.5 million emigrated to Britain and America. The majority of the people who died or emigrated came from the west and south of the country, from the poor, Gaelic-speaking communities like Baile Beag. This is the significance of Bridget's fear of the smell of rotting potatoes. Friel is reminding his audience that disaster awaits this community in the future.

www. CHECK THE NET

For information on Brian Friel's life, his plays and a helpful bibliography visit **http://www. eng.umu.se/lughn asa/brian.htm**

HEDGE-SCHOOLS

Hedge-schools were set up on an informal and makeshift basis in local communities throughout Ireland in response to the penal laws enacted by England preventing Irish Catholics and Dissenters from receiving an education. At first, they took place in hedgerows, with one pupil assigned to keep watch for English soldiers. The school master was paid small fees, sometimes by way of provisions and crops (or milk in Maire's case), for tuition in arithmetic, reading and writing. At the end of the eighteenth century, when the enforcement of the penal laws was relaxed in most areas, the hedge-schools moved into more permanent homes, such as barns or stables. In most of the hedge-schools instruction was given through the medium of the Irish language, and in many, Latin, Greek, mathematics and other subjects were taught too, particularly in the southwest of Ireland. There are a number of accounts of English travellers coming across classical scholars such as Hugh and Jimmy Jack in the midst of remote rural societies. School masters were well versed in most subjects, such as history, geography, the classical languages and literatures, mathematics, and the Irish and English languages. Some even knew and taught navigation, astronomy and surveying. Some were renowned Gaelic poets, whose teaching gave them a steady income and allowed them the leisure to write. The hedge-schools were also well served by textbooks and instruction manuals.

The hedge-schools were a form of rebellion against English colonial rule, and would certainly have been greeted with suspicion by English soldiers or civil servants. Most of the legitimate schools in Ireland had been created for the purposes of spreading the English language or the Anglican faith, so that the hedge-schools represented a threat to the establishment of an English, Protestant culture in Ireland. The hedge-schools were organised on a local basis only, but they spread rapidly across the country, and came from the desire among the peasants themselves for instruction. As Ireland became more anglicised in the later eighteenth century, the peasants increasingly felt the need to communicate in English, particularly for the purposes of trading at fairs and markets, and they put pressure on the hedge-school masters to instruct them and their children through the medium of English. This became the main language of most of the hedge-schools in the early nineteenth century. By the 1820s, the hedge-schools had become so widespread that the British government felt compelled to introduce a state system of education. Chief Secretary Stanley did so in 1831, creating what became known as the National Schools, which instructed

CONTEXT

Hugh's planned volume on languages, 'The Pentaglot Preceptor', was in fact a real book published by a school master in Dublin, Patrick Lynch, in 1796.

children through the medium of the English language solely and which charged no fees. This new system of national education made the hedge-schools redundant, and had a devastating effect on the use of the Gaelic language and indeed on the tradition of classical and historical learning in Ireland. However, even though the hedge-schools were a vital source of education and training in Ireland in the eighteenth and early nineteenth centuries, they did not benefit everyone. In Donegal, the setting of the play, some 62 per cent of the population were still illiterate in 1841.

ORDNANCE SURVEY

As a result of the British army's need for more accurate maps of Ireland, and as a result of growing dissatisfaction among taxpayers and government officials with existing, inadequate surveys of land sizes and values in Ireland, the British government consented to organise the first complete ordnance survey map of Ireland, at a scale of six inches to a mile. It was proclaimed that the map should be taken as 'proof of the disposition of the [British] legislature to adopt all measures calculated to advance the interests of Ireland' (Andrews, 1975, p. 308), as it showed that Britain was bringing the benefits of greater scientific knowledge of map-making and mathematics to Ireland. Many maps of Ireland had been made by previous generations of English settlers and soldiers, some for the purposes of marking out land which had been confiscated from the Irish, others for the purposes of providing the army with more accurate information about troubled areas. But none had been as complete or as accurate as the ordnance survey conducted between 1824 and 1846 under the direction of Colonel Thomas Colby of the Royal Engineers.

From the very beginning, the possibility of the survey being undertaken by Irish engineers and agents was dismissed, and the job was passed over to the ordnance survey unit of the Royal Engineers. Work began in the area in which the play is set, in the northwest of Ireland, in 1827 and was completed in 1840. Some of the maps from this area were published in 1833, however. In addition to producing a more accurate map, the engineers were also given the task of standardising the place names. They kept 'name-books' in which they recorded new names which they believed simplified and

CHECK THE NET
An interesting account of the Ordnance Survey in Donegal, beginning in 1824, is to be found at **http://www.finnvalley.ie/glenfin/** then click on Portraying Donegal: The Ordnance Survey Memoirs.

anglicised the spelling and pronunciation of the old Gaelic names. The government also employed an Irish scholar, John O'Donovan, to translate Gaelic names, and to standardise Gaelic spelling, much like Owen O'Donnell in the play.

The 'name-books' took longer to complete than the maps, largely because the survey teams were often divided about what names to give to townlands, particularly whether they should try to capture the meaning of Gaelic names (e.g. Bun na hAbhann, meaning foot of the river, might become 'riverfoot') or try to replicate the sound of the names in English spelling (e.g. Bun na hAbhann, pronounced Bun-na-how-en, might be simplified to Bunowen). Friel's play is largely accurate in its depiction of the work of the surveyors. Some of them, like Yolland in the play, did become interested in the history of the places which they were mapping, and were sensitive to what the local residents felt about name changes or about details of the map. Friel even borrows the names of the officers, Lancey and Yolland, from real officers who worked on the ordnance survey teams. Where real life differs from the play is that the engineers did not carry arms and were never called upon to conduct evictions, searches or any form of physical violence against the local populations. Friel seems to be conflating deliberately the destruction of Irish place names by the engineers with the destruction of Irish people's houses, farms and livelihoods by colonising soldiers.

NORTHERN IRELAND IN 1980

Translations was first produced in Derry in 1980, eleven years after the sectarian and political conflict in Northern Ireland began. Ireland had been partitioned into six northern counties and twenty-six southern counties in 1920, creating two separate states. The south became independent from Britain in 1922 while the north remained a colony of Britain with its own parliament. The six counties of Northern Ireland had been chosen because they contained a majority of Protestant people, who feared that they would be attacked and marginalised in independent, mostly Catholic, Ireland. As a result of partition, Protestants outnumbered Catholics in Northern Ireland by a ratio of 9:7, and electoral boundaries were established so as to ensure that Unionism, which most Protestant people supported, would always win. The Unionists held power in Northern Ireland from 1920 to 1972, during which time it failed to do anything to stop routine, institutionalised discrimination against Catholics in employment, housing, local government representation and in other basic civil rights, and failed to stop a sectarian police force from attacking and discriminating against Catholics. The Catholic people organised civil rights protests in the late 1960s, but were assaulted and beaten by loyalist gangs and paramilitary police units.

In response to the outrageous behaviour of the police, some Catholic areas of Derry and Belfast erected barricades and refused to allow police units to enter, but these areas were stormed by loyalist and police gangs. Violent clashes began to erupt across the province in 1969, and the British army was called in by the Unionist government to preserve the peace. A small minority of nationalists in Catholic areas, calling themselves the Provisional Irish Republican Army (IRA) saw this as the opportunity to use violence to overthrow the state, and began a campaign of guerrilla war against the army and police. Loyalist gangs responded to their attacks with more violence, and the war in Northern Ireland began. By 1980 many thousands of civilians, policemen, soldiers and gunmen had been killed or injured. In addition to the campaign of violence, IRA prisoners began to go on hunger strike to protest against the government's treatment of them as criminals rather than political prisoners. By the time *Translations* was produced, in September 1980, ten prisoners had starved themselves to death, and riots had erupted across Northern Ireland after every death. It was one of the worst years of violence and suffering in the history of the conflict.

Friel's play does not reflect directly on this context, but, in representing a struggle between the rebellious Donnelly twins and a colonial army in Act III, it does suggest a parallel with the conflict in Northern Ireland between the IRA and the British army. The characters of the play also represent a broad spectrum of political views. Lancey is the determined and stiff officer, who is capable of ruthlessness when he feels that it is necessary. The Donnelly twins, although we never meet them, are obviously in the process of

> **CONTEXT**
>
> In 1979 alone, the IRA assassinated the Northern Ireland spokesman for the Conservative party, the British ambassador to the Netherlands and Earl Mountbatten, the former viceroy of India, and had killed eighteen soldiers of the Parachute Regiment in a bomb attack in south County Down.

CHECK THE NET

The CAIN (Conflict Archive on the Internet) site **http// cain.ulst.ac.uk** contains 'information and source material on the "Troubles" in Northern Ireland from 1968 to the present'. It is an excellent site which lists background, key events, key issues, and contains a superb chronology.

becoming hardened rebels, resolute in opposing the army with hit-and-run raids. In between those two extremes, Yolland is the soldier who is liberal and sentimental about Ireland, Maire is the Irish girl who is sentimental about England, Doalty and Manus are sympathetic to the Donnelly twins but only take up violent or rebellious measures when they are pushed into it, and Hugh clings to his Gaelic traditions until he realises that they are becoming outdated. Each of these characters represents a potential response to the conflict in Northern Ireland – to toughen security measures, to take up arms against the state, or to compromise and make peace. Friel seems to favour those characters who are compromisers – Yolland, Maire and Hugh – who learn to love those from other cultures and to embrace other cultures for the possibilities they offer, rather than to spurn them out of fear. These characters have the capacity to put fear and the past behind them, and they have much to offer in the context of Northern Irish politics as role models of reconciliation.

CONTEMPORARY LANGUAGE DEBATES

Ireland is largely an English-speaking country today, despite the fact that the constitution of the Republic of Ireland claims that Gaelic is the first official language of the nation. It has been the aspiration of the Irish government, for much of the twentieth century, to revive the use of the Gaelic language. Gaelic is a compulsory part of primary and secondary education, for example, and successive governments have funded Gaelic language radio and television stations, and cultural organisations to promote fluency in the language. But Gaelic is still a minority language in Ireland, as was evident in a government survey of attitudes to the language in 1975. Only 2.7 per cent of Irish people were found to have 'native speaker' ability, and a further 10.8 per cent could understand 'most conversations'. In contrast, some 80 per cent of Irish people were shown to be consistently indifferent to the Gaelic language. In contrast, the census of 2002 showed over 1.5 million speakers of Irish in the state, out of a population of just under 4 million. These statistics showed that, even when Ireland was independent from Britain, and its people were free to speak or learn whichever language they chose, the majority of them did not know or use the Gaelic language, but that the situation is slowly changing.

Translations was written in the aftermath of the government survey, at a time when there was intense debate about the future of the Gaelic language. As Declan Kiberd has argued, 'the play is an uncompromising reminder that it is Irish, and not English people, who have the power to decide which language is spoken in Ireland' (Kiberd, 1995, p. 616). The play asks audiences to believe that much of the dialogue is in the Gaelic language, but this is an indictment of the lack of knowledge of the language among Irish audiences. If the play is about the decline of a language which has been devastated and made almost redundant, Friel is also highlighting the **irony** of having to tell the story of this tragedy in the language which replaced Gaelic, an irony of which he is very well aware. The Irish audiences might laugh at the inability of Yolland and Lancey to communicate in Gaelic to the villagers, but the play is also showing those audiences that they are in the same position as the English soldiers, needing to have Gaelic, as well as Greek and Latin, translated into English for them.

QUESTION

How many different kinds of translation are contained in the play?

LITERARY BACKGROUND

Brian Friel was one of a number of writers in Northern Ireland who sought to explain the violence and conflict of the 1970s. The divisions and tensions in Northern Ireland since 1969 forced writers such as Friel, Seamus Heaney, Tom Paulin and John Montague to examine their own cultural histories and identities for the causes and the possible solutions to 'the troubles'. Heaney, for example, through poems such as 'The Tollund Man' and 'The Bog Queen', explored images of ancient murder victims discovered in bogs as a means of describing and understanding the horror of violence and killing in contemporary Northern Ireland. Heaney suggested that poetry could be a kind of excavation of cultural identity, with the poet digging through the soil of history to uncover the roots of modern disturbances. Friel might be seen as using the form of drama to explore the relevance for contemporary Ireland of the myths and conflicts of the past, and he does this in a number of his plays, most notably *Translations*, *Making History* and *Volunteers*.

CHECK THE NET

Go to **http://www.rte.ie/radio/readingthefuture** for an RTE documentary on Brian Friel and Field Day.

Ireland is historically divided into four provinces: Munster, Leinster, Connaught, and Ulster (most of which is under British rule). Tom Paulin, Northern poet and Field Day director, proposed a 'fifth province', a province of the mind, to which allegiance could be given, where the history and art and politics of Ireland could be debated without the constraints of existing conflicting traditions.

As language and names are contentious issues in Northern Ireland, with the very name of the province and some of its towns the subject of fierce argument, it is not surprising to find Northern Irish writers fascinated with the history of linguistic traditions and changes in place names. John Montague published a poem in 1972 called 'A Lost Tradition' which mourned the loss of Gaelic place names. He wrote: 'The whole landscape a manuscript / We had lost the skill to read / A part of our past disinherited'. In the same year he published his great poem-cycle on the Troubles and history, *The Rough Field*, the title itself a literal translation of the poet's native Garvaghey (*garbh achaidh*, a rough field) in county Tyrone. It is this feeling of disinheritance from their own cultural traditions which writers such as Montague, Heaney and Friel have explored as a way of articulating the problems with cultural identity for the people of Northern Ireland. The Catholic people of the province felt that they had been dispossessed of the Gaelic language, while among the Protestant people there were sizeable numbers who had once spoken Ulster-Scots. Tom Paulin proposed a compromise solution to the language question by advocating the use of **Hiberno-English** as a literary language.

THE FIELD DAY THEATRE COMPANY

Most of these writers were involved in the Field Day Theatre Company, which was founded in 1980 by Brian Friel and Stephen Rea. The reasons for setting up a theatre company were initially expedient, in order to qualify for funding the production of Friel's *Translations* in Derry city. But the company became a lively stimulant of debates and artistic experiments in Ireland. In the programme notes for the first production of *Translations* Friel and Rea gave the following definition of the term 'Field Day' to convey the variety of senses in which they felt the name was appropriate.

'Field day' could be about rehearsing strategies, celebrating strength, having fun or exploring nature. As a theatre company and a literary and cultural movement it did all these things. It experimented with cultural identities and histories within the context of Northern Irish politics. Its board of directors consisted of three Protestants and three Catholics, and it did try on several occasions to produce plays and pamphlets which reflected the diverse traditions of Northern Ireland, not just one side of the story. They produced innovative new plays and translations of foreign plays regularly throughout the 1980s and 1990s. They initiated a series of pamphlets on key themes in the cultural debates in Ireland in 1983, which included essays on Anglo-Irish identities, the language debates, cultural stereotypes, nationalism, unionism and colonialism. More recently, they produced a five-volume anthology of Irish writing, volumes one to three dealing with literature from ancient to modern times, volumes four and five, when published, deal with women's writing and traditions. Field Day also launched a series of academic books on Irish history, culture and literature.

An important dimension of the Field Day projects was that it was based in Derry. The city was an unusual choice, as it was in the northwest corner of Ireland and had traditionally not been regarded as a cultural centre. But it was a city divided in its very name, called Derry by Catholic or nationalist people, and Londonderry by Protestant or unionist people. It was also a frontier city, and had been built in the seventeenth century as a fort to protect English settlers from Irish attacks. It is still a frontier city now, as it lies on the border between the North and the Republic of Ireland. It seemed to be an appropriate city for a theatre company which was interested in healing divisions to begin. Almost every Field Day play premiered in Derry first, before embarking on a tour of London, New York and on tours of provincial towns in Ireland. The directors of Field Day wanted to move away from the idea of drama that could only be seen in the big cities. The theatre company became controversial for its productions, not least because Friel's own plays generated storms of debate about history and cultural identities. It seems to have been partly as a result of these controversies that Friel resigned from the company in 1994.

IRISH DRAMA

Irish drama of the twentieth century has been persistently concerned with a number of key themes and techniques, and Friel's *Translations* follows in the same tradition:

> **CONTEXT**
>
> *Field day*: A day on which troops are drawn up for an exercise in field manoeuvres; a military review; a day occupied with brilliant or exciting events; a triumph; a day spent in the field, e.g. by the hunt, or by field naturalists.

The rural west as a haven of Gaelic language and customs

This tradition began with W.B. Yeats, Lady Gregory and John M. Synge at the Abbey Theatre in the early years of the twentieth century. Synge in particular presented the west of Ireland as the source of a poor but exotic lifestyle which was alternative in language, morality, social customs and cultural habits to the anglicised east. The tradition was followed by a host of lesser playwrights, including M. J. Molloy, T. C. Murray, and John B. Keane.

Friel's play is set in a rural community in the northwest of Ireland, and it does seem to represent the last vestiges of a dying Gaelic community.

CONTEXT

Modern Irish drama is sometimes referred to in terms of 'waves'. The First Wave was the Gaelic literary revival, led by Yeats and Lady Gregory, and included Synge and O'Casey, although he was a transitional figure. The Second Wave includes contemporaries of Friel, Keane, Leonard, Behan. The Third Wave includes the younger generation of Irish playwrights, Marina Carr, Conor McPherson and Martin McDonagh.

The motivations and aspirations of Irish nationalism

Yeats is clearly interested in what makes people take up arms for a nationalist cause, in his play *Cathleen Ni Houlihan*, for example. Sean O'Casey also explored this theme in his Dublin trilogy of plays. Yeats had a heroic vision of sacrifice, while O'Casey is deeply cynical about any cause which resulted in the death of innocent people. Friel investigates the motivation for nationalist action by showing us the gradual turn of men like Manus, Owen and Doalty away from being friendly to English soldiers to being willing to fight against them. Younger playwrights such as Frank McGuinness explore the friction between the traditions on the island, in plays such as *Carthaginians* and *Behold the Sons of Ulster Marching Towards the Somme*.

The tragedy of key moments in Irish history

Yeats, O'Casey, and Frank McGuinness are good examples of dramatists who have turned back to the past to reflect on the significance of those events for the present, and who have explored the sentiments and perceptions surrounding key historical events. The events of early nineteenth-century Irish history, including the decline of the Gaelic language, the approach of famine, the imposition of tough colonial rule and the rise in the number of Irish people emigrating, are all reflected in *Translations*.

Materialist England and spiritual Ireland

A strong theme in Yeats's plays is the difference between mystical, artistic Ireland and England, which he spurned as shallow and materialistic. In Friel's play Hugh voices this same view.

The use of comedy to undermine authority figures

Sean O'Casey makes fun out of nationalist heroes, in particular, showing us that men who brag about their exploits in warfare are hollow and pathetic. Brendan Behan took this several steps further by making fun of every form of authority – policemen, soldiers, nationalists, civil servants, government officials, priests, prison warders, the upper class, and so on. Friel uses comedy to undermine Hugh, the school master, and Lancey and Yolland, the two officers.

Language as a medium of cultural and political identity

The invention of a peculiar language which indicated a difference between Irish and English cultural identities was the achievement of the earliest Anglo-Irish drama of the seventeenth and eighteenth centuries, with dramatists such as George Farquhar, Thomas Sheridan and Charles Macklin inventing a special inflection of English which indicated to audiences that the characters were Irish. Yeats and Synge partly continued this tradition by inflecting the English of their characters towards **Hiberno-English**. These dramatists were also accused of making fun of Irish speech, however, and of falsifying Irish ways of speaking. Friel sidesteps this problem by having his characters speaking in English, with hardly a trace of dialect except in the odd colloquial phrase, but having his audience believe that some of them are speaking in Gaelic.

The role of violence in Irish society and history

Almost all Irish dramatists in the twentieth century have been preoccupied with incidents of violence in Irish society and history, perhaps because this century has seen two lengthy guerrilla wars, the last of which, in Northern Ireland beginning in 1969, has led many writers to assess the place of violence in Ireland. Yeats, Synge, Gregory, O'Casey, Behan and John B. Keane, to name just a few, have explored the theme of violence. Friel is obviously concerned with the force of colonial violence in *Translations*.

CONTEXT

One of the reasons the Gaelic language is still compulsory in Irish schools is the extent to which it is thought that it distinguishes Irish people from British people. One of the leaders of the 1916 Rising, Padraic Pearse, made the often-repeated comment: 'A country without a language is a country without a soul'. This statement, which must come as a great surprise to Canadians, Swiss, Australians and the like, has become a cultural given.

Events in Ireland	Author's life	Literary events
1603 Enforcement of English law throughout Ireland		
1641 Great Catholic-Gaelic Rebellion		
1649 Cromwell arrives in Ireland		
1650 Catholic landowners exiled		
1690 William of Orange defeats James II at Battle of the Boyne		**1690-1780** Golden Age of Gaelic Aisling poetry
1695 First penal laws enacted against Catholics		
1775 Birth of Daniel O'Connell, campaigner for Catholic emancipation		
		1780 Brian Merriman, *The Midnight Court*
1798 Rebellion of the United Irishmen		
1800 Ireland annexed to Britain in Act of Union		**1800** Maria Edgeworth, *Castle Rackrent*
1816-42 16 crop failures due to potato blight		
1823 O'Connell's Catholic Association founded		
1824-46 Ordnance survey of Ireland		
1829 Catholic Emancipation Act passed (Catholics can now sit as MPs)		**1829** Gerald Griffin, *The Collegians*
1831 Creation of National Schools		
1833 First Ordnance Survey maps of Ireland published		
1841 Irish population reaches 8 million		
1845-9 The Great Famine: 1 million die; 1.5 million emigrate		
1847 Ireland left to 'operation of natural causes'; Death of O'Connell		**1847** William Carleton, *The Black Prophet*
		1852 Birth of Lady Augusta Gregory, leading figure in Irish Revival
		1856 Birth of George Bernard Shaw

Events in Ireland	Author's life	Literary events
1858 Irish Republican Brotherhood founded; Fenian Brotherhood founded in America		
		1863 Ferguson, *Lays of Western Gael*
		1865 Birth of W.B. Yeats
1867 Fenian rising in Ireland		**1871** Birth of J.M. Synge
1879 Threat of famine and evictions in Ireland		
		1880 Birth of Sean O'Casey
		1882 Birth of James Joyce
1886 First Home Rule Bill		
1891 Death of Charles Stewart Parnell		
1893 Second Home Rule Bill; foundation of Gaelic League		**1893** Douglas Hyde, *Love Songs of Connacht*
		1899 Irish Literary Theatre founded
		1900 Birth of Sean O'Faolain, Irish novelist and short story writer
		1902 W.B. Yeats, *Cathleen Ni Houlihan*
		1903 Birth of Frank O'Connor, Irish short story writer
		1904 G.B. Shaw, *John Bull's Other Island*
		1907 J.M. Synge, *Playboy of the Western World*
1912 Third Home Rule Bill: Ulster Volunteer Force founded; Irish Citizens Army and Irish National Volunteers founded		
1914-18 First World War		**1914** George Moore, *Hail and Farewell*
1916 Easter rising, Dublin		
1919 Anglo-Irish Treaty		
1922-3 Civil War; deaths of Michael Collins, Erskine Childers, Liam Lynch, Rory O'Connor		**1923** Birth of Brendan Behan
		1924 Sean O'Casey's *Juno and the Paycock* (Abbey)

Events in Ireland	Author's life	Literary events
		1926 O'Casey's *The Plough and the Stars* – riots accompany performance
	1929 Birth of **Brian Friel**, near Omagh, Co. Tyrone, N. Ireland	
		1932 Death of Lady Gregory
1937 Constitution of 'Eire' - southern Ireland becomes independent of Britain		
1939 IRA bombing campaign in Britain	**1939** Friel family move to Derry	**1939** Death of W.B. Yeats; birth of Seamus Heaney
1939-45 Second World War		
	1941-46 Secondary education at St Columb's College, Derry	**1941** Death of James Joyce
		1942 Patrick Kavanagh, *The Great Hunger*
	1946-48 Seminarian in St Patrick's College, Maynooth. Graduates, but leaves before ordination	
1949 Republic of Ireland declared	**1949** Begins teacher training at St Joseph's, Belfast	
	1950 Teaches in Derry	**1950** Death of G. B. Shaw
	1952 Begins writing short stories	
	1954 Marries Anne Morrison	
		1955 Irish premiere of Samuel Beckett's *Waiting for Godot* (Pike, Dublin)
1956-62 IRA campaign in North		
	1958 First radio plays for BBC: *A Sort of Freedom; To This Hard House*	**1958** Brendan Behan's *The Hostage*
	1960 *A Doubtful Paradise* staged by the Group Theatre, Belfast. Leaves teaching to write full time	
		1961 Tom Murphy's *A Whistle in the Dark*
	1962 *The Enemy Within* staged by the Abbey Theatre, Dublin. *A Saucer of Larks* (short stories) published	

Events in Ireland	Author's life	Literary events
	1963 With Tyrone Guthrie in Minneapolis; *The Blind Mice* (Olympia Theatre, Dublin)	
	1964 *Philadelphia, Here I Come!* (Gaiety Theatre, Dublin)	**1964** Death of Brendan Behan
		1965 John B. Keane, *The Field*
	1966 *The Gold in the Sea* (short stories); *The Loves of Cass McGuire* (Helen Hayes Theatre NY)	**1966** New Abbey Theatre opens, with smaller Peacock Theatre adjoining
	1967 *Lovers* (Gate Theatre, Dublin)	
1968 First Civil Rights March	**1968** *Crystal and Fox* (Gaiety)	
1969 Outbreak of sectarian and political conflict, N Ireland	**1969** *The Munday Scheme* (Olympia)	**1969** Howard Brenton, *The Romans in Britain* (play)
	1971 *The Gentle Island* (Olympia)	
1972 'Bloody Sunday' in Derry		**1972** John Montague, 'A Lost Tradition', *The Rough Field*
	1973 *The Freedom of the City* (Royal Court)	
	1975 *Volunteers* (Abbey)	**1975** Seamus Heaney, *North*
	1977 *Living Quarters* (Abbey)	
	1979 *Faith Healers* (Longacre Theatre NY); *Aristocrats* (Abbey)	
1980 Ten prisoners starve to death; riots N Ireland	**1980** With Stephen Rea founds Field Day Theatre Co; **Translations** opens in Derry	
	1981 Version of Chekhov's *Three Sisters* (Guildhall, Derry)	
	1982 *The Communication Cord* (Guildhall, Derry). Friel moves from Muff to Greencastle, Co Donegal	
		1983 Tom Paulin, *The Liberty Tree*; Tom Murphy, *The Gigli Concert* (Abbey)

Events in Ireland	Author's life	Literary events
1985 Anglo-Irish Agreement		**1985** Frank McGuinness, *Observe the Sons of Ulster Marching Towards the Somme*
		1986 Thomas Kilroy, *Double Cross* (Field Day, Derry)
	1987 Friel's version of Turgenev's *Fathers and Sons* (Lyttleton, London). Appointed to Irish Senate	**1987** Stewart Parker, *Pentecost*
	1988 *Making History* (Guildhall, Derry)	
	1990 *Dancing at Lughnasa* (Abbey)	**1989** Death of Samuel Beckett
		1991 Movie version of Keane's *The Field*
	1992 Version of Macklin's *The True Born Irishman* entitled *The London Vertigo*. Version of Turgenev's *A Month in the Country* (Gate)	
1993 Northern Ireland Peace Process begins	**1993** *Wonderful Tennessee* (Abbey)	**1993** Frank McGuinness, *Someone Who'll Watch Over Me* (Abbey)
	1994 *Molly Sweeney* (Gate); Friel resigns from Field Day	**1994** Marina Carr, *The Mai* (Peacock)
		1996 Martin McDonagh, *The Beauty Queen of Leenane, A Skull in Connemara* (Druid, Galway)
	1997 *Give Me Your Answer, Do!* (Abbey)	**1997** Conor McPherson, *The Weir* (London); McDonagh, *The Lonesome West*
1998 GoodFriday Agreement	**1998** Version of Chekhov's *Uncle Vanya* (Gate). Movie version of *Dancing at Lughnasa*	
1999 New Devolved Government formed in Northern Ireland		
		2000 Marina Carr, *On Raftery's Hill* (Druid, Galway)
	2002 *Three Plays After*, versions of Chekhov (Gate)	
	2003 *Performances* (Gate)	**2003** Conor McPherson directs his script for the movie *The Actors*

OTHER WORKS BY BRIAN FRIEL

The Communication Cord, Gallery Press, 1983

Dancing at Lughnasa Faber and Faber, 1990

The Gold in the Sea (short stories), Gollancz, 1966

Making History, Faber and Faber, 1988

A Saucer of Larks (short stories), Gollancz, 1962

Selected Plays, Faber and Faber, 1984
    Includes *Philadelphia, Here I Come, The Freedom of the City, Living Quarters, Aristocrats, Faith Healer, Translations*

CRITICAL STUDIES OF FRIEL'S PLAYS

Elmer Andrews, *The Art of Brian Friel: Neither Dream nor Reality*, Macmillan, 1995

Tony Corbett, *Brian Friel: Decoding the Language of the Tribe*, The Liffey Press, 2002
    This book looks at Friel's plays in terms of their linguistic concerns, and with the connection in them between language and reality

Ulf Dantanus, *Brian Friel: A Study*, Faber and Faber, 1988

Paul Delaney, ed., *Brian Friel in Conversation*, University of Michigan, 2000
    This is a collection of interviews with Friel, in which he comments on his own plays and on their critical reception

George O'Brien, *Brian Friel*, Gill and Macmillan, 1989

Alan Peacock, ed., *The Achievement of Brian Friel*, Colin Smythe, 1993
    All useful studies

Richard Pine, *Brian Friel and Ireland's Drama*, Routledge, 1990
    Pine's book surveys Friel's writings since the 1950s, examining each play and short-story collection in detail. He argues that Friel's *Philadelphia, Here I Come!* marks the beginning of contemporary Irish drama

FRIEL'S SOURCES AND SECONDARY READING

J. H. Andrews, *A Paper Landscape: The Ordnance Survey of Nineteenth-Century Ireland*, Oxford University Press, 1975.
    An impressive and comprehensive study of the ordnance survey campaigns in Ireland from 1824 to 1846, Andrews covers the contexts, organisation, methods and results of the campaigns in detail. Friel was fascinated with the ideals and problems of representing the landscape in such detail on a map

Edmund Curtis, *A History of Ireland*, Methuen, 1936
Curtis's history covers a vast sweep of Irish history and has been one of the standard accounts of Irish history since it was first published. Friel quotes from Curtis's book in the programme notes to *Translations*

P.J. Dowling, *The Hedge Schools of Ireland*, Mercier Press, 1968
Dowling's short history of the hedge-schools covers the emergence of the schools as a response to the penal laws, how the schools worked and what subjects were taught there, the nature of the school masters, and the decline of the hedge-school in the early nineteenth century. Many of the details of Friel's school in *Translations* are evidently borrowed from this book

Michael Herity, ed., Preface by Brian Friel, *Ordnance Survey Letters: Donegal*, Dublin: Four Masters Press, 2000.
This is a collection of letters written by John O'Donovan, on whom Owen is partly based, during the survey of Donegal

George Steiner, *After Babel: Aspects of Language and Translation*, Oxford University Press, 1975
An influential study of the idea of languages and translation, Steiner's book argues that translation is an activity which we conduct almost every minute of the day and that translation can never be perfect or adequate. Steiner explains theories of language and translation lucidly and simply, and refers to an impressive range of languages and cultures. Friel read and was greatly inspired by this book

IRISH DRAMA

Michael Etherton, *Contemporary Irish Dramatists*, Macmillan, 1989
Etherton traces the history of Irish drama from the 1960s to the 1980s, and devotes a lengthy chapter, almost a quarter of the book, to the plays of Brian Friel. Etherton argues that Friel has been instrumental in some of the most exciting developments in contemporary Irish drama

Christopher Murray, *Twentieth Century Irish Drama: Mirror up to Nation*, Manchester University Press, 1997
Murray argues that Irish drama has reflected and shaped the tremendous changes in Irish politics and society in the twentieth century. He examines Friel's role in this process in a chapter on how contemporary dramatists have reflected on the violence and politics of Northern Ireland since 1969

Marilynn J. Richtarik, *Acting Between the Lines: The Field Day Theatre Company and Irish Cultural Politics 1980–1984*, Clarendon Press, Oxford, 1994
This is a detailed study of the Field Day Theatre Company including the history of its formation and the projects with which it was involved in the first four years of its existence. It includes a chapter on *Translations* which examines the controversies surrounding the historical inaccuracies of the play and the criticisms made in the early reviews

FURTHER READING

Anthony Roche, *Contemporary Irish Drama: From Beckett to McGuinness*, Gill and Macmillan, 1994
> This book examines the popularity and success of Irish drama since the work of Brendan Behan and Samuel Beckett in the 1950s. It includes chapters on Brian Friel, Thomas Kilroy, Tom Murphy and Northern Irish drama, and celebrates in particular the work of Frank McGuinness

LITERARY AND HISTORICAL BACKGROUND

J.H. Andrews, *Shapes of Ireland: Maps and their Makers 1564–1839*, Geography Publications, 1997
> A study of the chequered history of English map-making in Ireland, Andrews's book explores in depth the methods, motives and means by which maps were made of Ireland from the sixteenth to the nineteenth century. It includes a chapter on the ordnance survey maps of the early nineteenth century

S.J. Connolly, ed., *The Oxford Companion to Irish History*, Oxford University Press, 1998
> This book contains entries on key historical events, figures and trends in Ireland, and may be useful in contextualising some elements of Friel's *Translations*. It includes entries on hedge-schools, National Schools, the ordnance survey and on Gaelic Ireland

Reg Hindley, *The Death of the Irish Language*, Routledge, 1990
> Hindley's book traces the decline of the Gaelic language from the eighteenth to the twentieth century, and examines the causes of this decline. It also analyses regional differences in how the language has survived, and explores the various strategies employed in attempting to keep the language alive

A. Norman Jeffares, *Anglo-Irish Literature*, Macmillan, 1982
> Jeffares's study of Irish writing in English is comprehensive and detailed, and analyses the emergence of this tradition of literature from the medieval to the modern period. He barely mentions Friel, but it is a useful guide to the history of Anglo-Irish literature

Robert Kee, *Ireland: A History*, Weidenfeld & Nicolson, 1980.
> A useful, highly illustrated potted history based on the BBC/RTE television series

Declan Kiberd, *Inventing Ireland: The Literature of the Modern Nation*, Jonathan Cape, 1995
> Kiberd's book contains illuminating chapters on Northern Irish writers, and the literary and political contexts in which Friel was writing, as well as an excellent interpretation of Friel's *Translations*. It constructs a careful reading of the play as an exploration of the impact of colonialism and of the various attempts at resistance

Robert Welch, ed., *The Oxford Companion to Irish Literature*, Oxford University Press, 1996
> This book contains entries on key Irish writers, writings, terms and concepts, and may be useful when considering Friel in relation to the Irish literary tradition. It includes commentaries on Friel and his works, as well as entries on many of Friel's plays

THE THEATRE

Keir Elam, *The Semiotics of Theatre*, Methuen, 1984
> Whilst very dense, it contains useful tools for dissecting the problems of plays

alienation the feeling of being estranged or isolated, or not at home. It is not just the experience of being an outsider, but can also involve feeling estranged from one's own home, friends, or society. In dramatic terms, alienation can be cultivated in the theatre among audiences in order to prevent them from identifying with particular characters or actions so that they can make their interpretations objectively

antiquity the condition of being able to trace ancient forms and objects, and of belonging to age-old patterns of living and thinking. It involves ignoring the latest changes in all or any fields (e.g. science, dress, art, politics) and paying attention only to how the ancient world lived

bathos a comic comedown, a deliberate anticlimax, used by authors to undercut characters or situations

characterisation the way in which a writer creates characters in a narrative or drama so as to attract or repel our sympathy

classics from the Latin for 'writing of the highest quality'. Because western critics have often regarded ancient Greek and Roman literary works as the models for excellence, 'classics' came to refer to 'ancient Greek and Roman' literature, culture and history in general

colloquialism relaxed, everyday language, rather than formalised or conventional language. Colloquialisms in literature will often be composed of the use of incorrect grammar, such as 'yous' instead of the plural 'you', and the incorporation of localised or regional language, like the words 'jackeen' or 'eejit' in Ireland. Slang is also part of colloquial language

colonialism and postcolonialism colonialism is the study of the imperial enterprise which appropriated territory, mostly in third world countries, as possessions of the colonising power. Generally, this enterprise is analysed from the perspective of the imperial power, whose interaction with the colony is seen as benevolent. Postcolonialism, on the other hand, is the study of the imperial enterprise from the perspective of the colonised. In particular, postcolonial theory examines the political dimension of colonial literature and educational practices in terms of their perpetuation of colonial hegemony on colonised peoples

deconstruction a blanket title for certain radical critical theories which revise and develop the tenets of structuralism. One proponent, Jacques Derrida, argues that a speaker cannot fully possess the significance of the words he is speaking. The assumption that he can (even where there is not even the consciousness of the speaker present to validate meaning) has, however, dominated western thought, and it should be the aim of the philosopher and critic to 'deconstruct' the philosophy and literature of the past to show this false assumption and reveal the essential **paradox** at the heart of language. Any individual statement depends for its meaning on its relationship with its surrounding system of language and it can only derive its meaning by its difference from all the other possible meanings epic specifically, epic refers to a long narrative poem featuring superhuman heroes, but more generally 'epic' can refer to any piece of literature or drama which involves myths and legends about the foundation and transformation of national communities. Friel's *Translations* might be called a national epic according to this loose definition of the term

Hiberno-English varieties of English spoken in Ireland, where standard English has been altered by contact with the grammatical structures, vocabularies, sound systems, pronunciations and patterns of intonation of the Gaelic language

historical drama a type of drama which is set in a particular historical period, and which dramatises events and attitudes of that period. Both real and imaginary persons may appear as characters

imagery (Latin 'copy, representation') a critical word with several different applications. In its narrowest sense an 'image' is a word-picture, a description of some visible scene or object. More commonly, however, 'imagery' refers to the figurative language in a piece of literature (metaphors and similes); or all the words which refer to objects and qualities which appeal to the senses and feelings

irony/ironic saying something while deliberately meaning something completely opposite, or implying a different meaning by understatement and allusion. In *Translations*, Hugh speaks in pompous, eloquent statements about the richness of Gaelic language and literature compensating for the poverty of its speakers, but a careful reading of the way in which he makes these statements may reveal that he says them only to make fun of Yolland's naïve romantic attitudes towards Ireland

malapropism the unwitting use of improper or muddled words, deployed by the author for comic effect – from Mrs Malaprop in Sheridan's *The Rivals*

modernity the condition of being in current fashion or being in touch with the most recent developments in all or any fields (e.g. science, dress, art, politics). It may also mean a healthy disrespect for anything antiquated and a keen interest in experimenting with newness

paradox an apparently self-contradictory statement, which behind its seeming absurdity has a meaning or truth

parody an imitation of a specific work or literature or style devised so as to ridicule its characteristic features

subtext a situation that lies behind the behaviour of characters in a play, but to which no one refers explicitly and which may never be fully explained

symbolism objects or images which come to stand for something else. A tree, for example, can symbolise strength or tradition, while white lilies conventionally symbolise death or mourning. Symbolist literature tends to emphasise the importance of using private and conventional symbols to create a wider meaning or world-view

tragedy the genre in literature and drama which conventionally involves works in which an individual is seen to have a lamentable downfall, sometimes as a scapegoat or as a sacrifice. In *Translations*, a whole community is the subject of a tragic downfall, as its culture and ways of life are seen to be sacrificed to make way for the desires of its conquerors

AUTHORS OF THESE NOTES

John Brannigan is College Lecturer in English at University College Dublin. His most recent publications include a book on the writings of Brendan Behan, and two books on postwar English literature. He has published essays on a wide range of Irish and British writings. He is currently working on a study of the contemporary English novelist, Pat Barker.

Tony Corbett has lectured and published widely in the field of drama, from medieval English street plays to modern Irish theatre. He is the author of *Brian Friel: Decoding the Language of the Tribe*, 2002, and is currently working on a full-length study of late medieval drama.

General editor

Martin Gray, former Head of the Department of English Studies at the University of Stirling, and of Literary Studies at the University of Luton

Maya Angelou
I Know Why the Caged Bird Sings

Jane Austen
Pride and Prejudice

Alan Ayckbourn
Absent Friends

Elizabeth Barrett Browning
Selected Poems

Robert Bolt
A Man for All Seasons

Harold Brighouse
Hobson's Choice

Charlotte Brontë
Jane Eyre

Emily Brontë
Wuthering Heights

Shelagh Delaney
A Taste of Honey

Charles Dickens
David Copperfield
Great Expectations
Hard Times
Oliver Twist

Roddy Doyle
Paddy Clarke Ha Ha Ha

George Eliot
Silas Marner
The Mill on the Floss

Anne Frank
The Diary of a Young Girl

William Golding
Lord of the Flies

Oliver Goldsmith
She Stoops to Conquer

Willis Hall
The Long and the Short and the Tall

Thomas Hardy
Far from the Madding Crowd
The Mayor of Casterbridge
Tess of the d'Urbervilles
The Withered Arm and other Wessex Tales

L.P. Hartley
The Go-Between

Seamus Heaney
Selected Poems

Susan Hill
I'm the King of the Castle

Barry Hines
A Kestrel for a Knave

Louise Lawrence
Children of the Dust

Harper Lee
To Kill a Mockingbird

Laurie Lee
Cider with Rosie

Arthur Miller
The Crucible
A View from the Bridge

Robert O'Brien
Z for Zachariah

Frank O'Connor
My Oedipus Complex and Other Stories

George Orwell
Animal Farm

J.B. Priestley
An Inspector Calls
When We Are Married

Willy Russell
Educating Rita
Our Day Out

J.D. Salinger
The Catcher in the Rye

William Shakespeare
Henry IV Part I
Henry V
Julius Caesar
Macbeth
The Merchant of Venice
A Midsummer Night's Dream
Much Ado About Nothing

Romeo and Juliet
The Tempest
Twelfth Night

George Bernard Shaw
Pygmalion

Mary Shelley
Frankenstein

R.C. Sherriff
Journey's End

Rukshana Smith
Salt on the snow

John Steinbeck
Of Mice and Men

Robert Louis Stevenson
Dr Jekyll and Mr Hyde

Jonathan Swift
Gulliver's Travels

Robert Swindells
Daz 4 Zoe

Mildred D. Taylor
Roll of Thunder, Hear My Cry

Mark Twain
Huckleberry Finn

James Watson
Talking in Whispers

Edith Wharton
Ethan Frome

William Wordsworth
Selected Poems

A Choice of Poets

Mystery Stories of the Nineteenth Century including The Signalman

Nineteenth Century Short Stories

Poetry of the First World War

Six Women Poets

For the AQA Anthology:
Duffy and Armitage & Pre-1914 Poetry

Heaney and Clarke & Pre-1914 Poetry

Poems from Different Cultures

Margaret Atwood
Cat's Eye
The Handmaid's Tale

Jane Austen
Emma
Mansfield Park
Persuasion
Pride and Prejudice
Sense and Sensibility

Alan Bennett
Talking Heads

William Blake
Songs of Innocence and of Experience

Charlotte Brontë
Jane Eyre
Villette

Emily Brontë
Wuthering Heights

Angela Carter
Nights at the Circus

Geoffrey Chaucer
The Franklin's Prologue and Tale
The Merchant's Prologue and Tale
The Miller's Prologue and Tale
The Prologue to the Canterbury Tales
The Wife of Bath's Prologue and Tale

Samuel Coleridge
Selected Poems

Joseph Conrad
Heart of Darkness

Daniel Defoe
Moll Flanders

Charles Dickens
Bleak House
Great Expectations
Hard Times

Emily Dickinson
Selected Poems

John Donne
Selected Poems

Carol Ann Duffy
Selected Poems

George Eliot
Middlemarch
The Mill on the Floss

T.S. Eliot
Selected Poems
The Waste Land

F. Scott Fitzgerald
The Great Gatsby

E.M. Forster
A Passage to India

Brian Friel
Translations

Thomas Hardy
Jude the Obscure
The Mayor of Casterbridge
The Return of the Native
Selected Poems
Tess of the d'Urbervilles

Seamus Heaney
Selected Poems from 'Opened Ground'

Nathaniel Hawthorne
The Scarlet Letter

Homer
The Iliad
The Odyssey

Aldous Huxley
Brave New World

Kazuo Ishiguro
The Remains of the Day

Ben Jonson
The Alchemist

James Joyce
Dubliners

John Keats
Selected Poems

Philip Larkin
The Whitsun Weddings and Selected Poems

Christopher Marlowe
Doctor Faustus
Edward II

Arthur Miller
Death of a Salesman

John Milton
Paradise Lost Books I & II

Toni Morrison
Beloved

George Orwell
Nineteen Eighty-Four

Sylvia Plath
Selected Poems

Alexander Pope
Rape of the Lock & Selected Poems

William Shakespeare
Antony and Cleopatra
As You Like It
Hamlet
Henry IV Part I
King Lear
Macbeth
Measure for Measure
The Merchant of Venice
A Midsummer Night's Dream
Much Ado About Nothing
Othello
Richard II
Richard III
Romeo and Juliet
The Taming of the Shrew
The Tempest
Twelfth Night
The Winter's Tale

George Bernard Shaw
Saint Joan

Mary Shelley
Frankenstein

Jonathan Swift
Gulliver's Travels and A Modest Proposal

Alfred Tennyson
Selected Poems

Virgil
The Aeneid

Alice Walker
The Color Purple

Oscar Wilde
The Importance of Being Earnest

Tennessee Williams
A Streetcar Named Desire
The Glass Menagerie

Jeanette Winterson
Oranges Are Not the Only Fruit

John Webster
The Duchess of Malfi

Virginia Woolf
To the Lighthouse

William Wordsworth
The Prelude and Selected Poems

W.B. Yeats
Selected Poems

Metaphysical Poets